The World is About to Laugh Like it has Never Laughed Before

SO-AWX-054

Laughter has no language, knows no boundaries, does not discriminate between caste, creed and colour. It is a powerful emotion and has all the ingredients for uniting the entire world.

Mission: World Peace thru' Laughter

a ha ha ho ha ho ha ho ha ha
ho ha ha ha ha ho ha ho ho ha ha
o ho ha ha ho ha ha ho ha ho
ha ho ho

L A U G H
For No Reason

DR. MADAN KATARIA
Founder President
Laughter Club International

Copyright 1999 © by Dr. Madan Kataria. All rights reserved. No part of this may be reproduced in any form or by any electronic or mechanical means, without permission in writing from Madhuri International.

First Edition : 1999

Published by:
MADHURI INTERNATIONAL
A-1, Denzil, 3rd Cross Road,
Lokhandwala Complex,
Andheri (W), Mumbai - 400 053.
Tel: 022 - 631 6426 Fax: 022 - 632 4293
E-mail: laugh@vsnl.com or laugh@bom3.vsnl.net.in

ISBN 81-87529-00-8

Publishers are looking for experts to translate this book into all the languages all over the world. Those interested may send their details to the Madhuri International address given above.

QUANTITY SALES

This book is available at a special discount when purchased in bulk by corporations, organisations or groups. Special imprints, messages and excerpts can be produced to meet your needs.

WEBSITE ORDERS
You can also buy this book on our website : www.worldlaughtertour.com

For any other information write to:
Madhuri International,
A-1, Denzil, 3rd Cross Road,
Lokhandwala Complex, Andheri (W),
Mumbai - 400 053. INDIA

This book gives non-specific, general advice and should not be relied on as a substitute for proper medical consultation. The author and publisher cannot accept responsibility for illness arising out of the failure to seek medical advice from a doctor.

CONTENTS

BEFORE YOU BEGIN TO LAUGH WITH ME

A s I sat down to write this book, to spread the message of merry medicine all over the world, my doctor friends, authors and researchers asked me, "You are writing a book for international readers, you must be well read and thorough on the subject. Have you gone to the British Library? Did you refer to literature at the US Information Service? How many books you have read on laughter?"

To me it seemed that they were trying to scare me and tell me that it is not a joke to write a book. I told one of them that I had read more than four hundred books related to laughter to which his reaction was: "You must be kidding, I have never seen you reading, as most of the time you are busy with visits to Laughter Clubs all over the country". In reply, I told my friend that I had read books by Robert Holden, Prof. William Fry, Petty Wotten and Norman Cousins. Each one of them must have read hundreds of books before they wrote their treatises which contain the essence of those hundreds of books. Since the message of my book is going to be very simple, going through those hundreds of books myself seemed unnecessary to me.

I must also confess that I am not a person with an extraordinary sense of humor. Nor am I a comedian or a great joke teller. I am not a Yoga expert and am neither very well versed in the *Vedas,*

Upanishads or *Gita*. I am also not very good at writing. I am only a physician who comes from a large agricultural family, from a small village with a population of not more than five hundred. I have lived my childhood with rustic, innocent and hard working people. My experience with villagers taught me that laughter can come to you easily and in abundance if only you do not block it, which is what city dwellers do and thereby deny themselves the manifold benefits of that wonderful gift from God: the capacity to laugh.

The idea of starting a Laughter Club came to me as a flash and I am indeed very glad that I acted on that flash. The result is, what I would like to call, by now, a big movement. The 13th of March, 1995, was when the first Laughter Club was started and, in a little more than four years, this small seed has bloomed into a big, beautiful three-seventy clubs only in Mumbai and more than four hundred all over India. The amount of interest shown by several persons abroad leaves me with little doubt that the movement will spread and expand in their countries equally fast, perhaps even faster. And, it will not be very long before the slogan, namely "World Peace Through Laughter" for the first World Laughter Day held in Mumbai, on the 10th of January, 1998, becomes a reality.

It is neither my intention nor my effort to write anything very profound about laughter. I leave that to the more learned, the wise and the more competent. This book seeks to inform all those who would like to know what the concept of a Laughter Club is, how it started, what it seeks to do and achieve, what are its programmes and procedures, aims and objects, hopes and aspirations. An attempt is also being made to answer the queries and inquiries received, and allay the doubts raised from time to time. If any one wishes to seek further information or explanation or to offer any comment, he is most welcome to do so. It is our firm belief that one has to and must keep learning all the time. Only then is meaningful growth possible.

While various aspects of the Laughter Club and the queries and doubts have been suitably dealt with in different chapters of this book, it will, I think, not be out of place to mention here that, initially, Laughter Clubs aimed at making the benefits of laughter accessible, freely and free of cost, to one and all; seeing the potential of what good laughter can do. These aims have been revised to "Health and happiness through laughter and spirit of laughter", the spirit of laughter being making yourself and others also happy.

A number of people have said kind things about me. While I am very grateful to them, I must mention that it has, all along, been a combined effort to which so many have contributed. It will not be incorrect to say that each member of every Laughter Club has contributed, in one way or the other, to the growth of the movement of Laughter Clubs. My role has been only that of a facilitator.

DR. MADAN KATARIA
A-1, Denzil, 3rd Cross Road,
Lokhandwala Complex, Andheri (W),
Mumbai - 400 053. INDIA
Tel: 022 - 631 6426
Fax: 022 - 632 4293
E-mail: laugh@vsnl.com

ACKNOWLEDGMENTS

From just five persons on 13th of March,1995 to sixty Laughter Clubs in Mumbai and more than three hundred clubs all over India, hundreds of articles in all the world's prestigious publications the laughter story appearing on many television networks and thousands of request letters from all over the world for new Laughter Clubs, indicate that these clubs are indeed no laughing matter. This has certainly not been achieved me alone, I am not that capable. I would like to salute the Divine Force which has chosen to manifest itself through me. Though I did generate the concept of Laughter Clubs, the laughter movement has reached its current size and stature due to the untiring efforts of the following people, to whom I would like to extend my love and gratitude:

First and foremost, my loving wife Madhuri, who has dedicated her life to the cause. Another Laughologist who needs to be applauded is Mr. P.T. Hinduja, who understood the power behind laughter and worked tirelessly towards this cause, even at the age of 75. He has assisted me in hundreds of public demonstrations, talks and seminars on laughter. Often, while travelling, we brainstormed on various developments of the laughter movement. He has written articles in *Your Own Doctor* on Laughter and the Spirit of Laughter. He has been an eye witness to all the events that took place to fulfil the dream of making this planet a "Laughter Haven".

I can't forget the contribution of J.K. Kapur, Vice President of the Laughter Club International, who along with young, dynamic Mohit Kapoor, from Worli Laughter Club, helped to make my dream come true. When I was struggling to establish a suitable platform, they brought the "Laughter Club International" into existence and organised two big events, World Laughter Day and the Laughter Convention which shook the whole world with laughter.

I would like to thank anchor persons of a large number of Laughter Clubs who have put in tremendous efforts to spread this message all over the world. Among them are B.P.Hirani, Kamini Bathija (Joggers Park Bandra), G.P.Shethia, Manubhai Turakhia, J.C.Jain (Shivaji Park), Jeet Hans (Juhu Garden), Jagdish Mehra (Muktanand Park) S.N.Putatunda, an entire group of volunteers from Worli Laughter Club, Devendra Jaawre, Harish Puri (Nasik), L.N.Daga (Calcutta), S.K.Shrivastava (Nagpur), Dr. Mukund Mehta and A.P.Kumar (Ahmedabad), Shirin Punjwani (Hydrabad), Bhanu Bhandari (Ahmednagar), Suresh Rathi (Jodhpur), Pranita Talesra and Sunderlal Dak (Udaipur), Jasveen Anand(Kota) P.C.Sancoalcar (Goa).

I owe a fortune to Steve Wilson, a psychologist and America's popular joyologist, who was the first person to recognise the potential behind laughter. He landed in Mumbai and immediately put the laughter clubs movement on a world platform. Like me, he also wants to make people laugh all over the world and die laughing. He is a man with a vision to bring global happiness. His slogan "Think Globally, Laugh Locally" is great. My special thanks to Pam Wilson, who is helping us to organise the World Laughter Tour, which starts May 1999, from U.S.A. Thanks to Karyn Buxman for joining the laughter movement. Many thanks to Nari Motwani (New York), Arya Patharia (California), Mr. Gidwaney (Chicago) for helping to network laughter lovers in U.S.A. Thank you dear Francisca Munk and Heidi (Norway) for all your help and encouragement.

CHAPTER - 1

Yogic Laughter - A BREAKTHROUGH!

Over the past two decades, extensive research has been conducted all over the world and it has been proved that laughter has a positive impact on various systems of the body. Scientists are convinced that laughter has both preventive and therapeutic value. But these days, where is laughter? It seems that people have forgotten to laugh. Normally, people believe that you need a good sense of humour to laugh, but the reverse is also true. You try to laugh in a group for no reason, your inhibitions are broken and sense of humour flows. This is exactly the breakthrough we have achieved in our Laughter Clubs.

For the first time we have developed a new technique of thought free group laughter based on yoga (Hasya Yoga). Anyone can participate in group laughter, everyday for 15-20 minutes, without resorting to jokes. Each laughter session starts with deep breathing

and the Ho-Ho, Ha-Ha exercise, followed by a variety of stimulated laughter like hearty laughter, silent laughter, medium laughter, lion laughter, swinging laughter, one meter laughter, cocktail laughter and many other kinds.

LAUGH AND DEVELOP A SENSE OF HUMOUR

A sense of humour is the capacity of an individual to perceive, relate and experience a given situation in a more funny and humourous way. A sense of humour is not that one is born with, but it is a skill which can be acquired with practice. One thing that God has given everyone of us is a tremendous potential to laugh. As you can see, a child can laugh upto 300-400 times a day. The child does not laugh because it has a sense of humour, but because it is in the nature of the child to be joyful. As and when the child starts growing and he is exposed to more and more information, his laughter starts getting lost under layers of seriousness, self control, responsibility, fear and insecurity. As a result, an ordinary situation at which the child used to be amazed and amused, does not trigger any good feeling.

To develop sense of humour, one needs to remove the layers of inhibition and the mental blocks which have been created by oneself, one's parents and society. Once these barriers are removed, the infinite potential to laugh will unfold automatically and a sense of humour starts flowing. Teaching a person who has a lot of inhibitions to develop a sense of humour, is like flushing a drain which is blocked with rubble. Once you remove the blockade, water will start flowing. This is exactly what has happened in Laughter Clubs. It is for this reason that we are successful in making thousands of people laugh in a country like India where people hardly laugh or smile.

The same people who never used to smile have started cracking jokes and enjoying jokes in a better way than before. They have started being playful and creative. If I had to teach them a sense of humour, I would have had to wait for eternity to see them laughing. Here nobody was first trained to have sense of humour and then laughed. We all laughed and laughed for no reason and without applying much logic. Therefore, it is not always the sense of humour which leads to laughter but laughter can also help you to develop a sense of humour.

Humour and laughter has a cause and effect relationship. Sometimes the humour is the cause, laughter is the effect. But in Laughter Clubs, laughter is the cause and a sense of humour is the effect. This goes in a circle and one can enter at any stage. Sometimes cause becomes effect and other times effect becomes cause. Somehow for Indians and perhaps for everyone in the world, it is much easier to laugh without bothering much about the existence or not of a sense of humour. Humour and laughter make one unity, each flows into the other. By volunteering to laugh in a group we are preparing the grounds for a sense of humour to flow. Therefore, if I and you don't have a sense of humour don't worry. Laugh yourself silly and your sense of humour will start flowing. Laughter Clubs are the ideal platforms to laugh your way to silliness, because there is no fear of ridicule by anyone.

FOCUS OF LAUGHTER

Ever since Laughter Clubs became popular, many journalists and laughter lovers from all over the world have visited India to study this phenomenon. I spoke with them for long hours about laughter and humour. I have never been anywhere abroad but as I read various books, I gained in the impression that people in the west are laying too much stress on developing a sense of humour so as to create laughter. They are trying different techniques to develop a sense of humour and rely upon some aids to create laughter. There are laughter clinics, people are clowning in hospitals and developing mirth aid kits to promote healing. The focus of laughter is more peripheral and is the object of humour. But it is also true that after watching a funny object a few times, one tends to become immune to it and the same thing might not look funny anymore.

Moreover, you will laugh as long as there is someone to make you laugh. What about afterwards? We need to develop our own inner resources, so that we can laugh and be amused whenever required. Therefore, the focus of laughter should be inside us rather that outside. If we can develop the capacity to laugh at ourselves and with others, it will lead to breaking down of big egos and promote peace.

The laughter arising from outside can sometime be negative. It needs to be handled carefully as it is like a double edged weapon. Therefore, the main center of laughter should be within you and it should flow from within to outside.

LIBERATING YOUR LAUGHTER FROM REASON

Normally, people look for some reason to laugh, but these days, because of the stress and strain of modern living, there are very few things which make us laugh and there are hundreds of things which can make us frown, howl and cry. Like laughter, happiness has also become conditional. Our happiness depends upon so many preconditions. Our happiness and laughter has become dependent on material success and personal achievements.

Laughter is an expression of happiness. If we can learn to laugh unconditionally, our happiness too will become unconditional. It is easier said than done. But if we practice in a group, we can make things happen rather than waiting for them to happen. If you laugh in a group you need not have any reason to laugh. It is contagious and comes out easily if done with proper training. Laughter in Laughter Clubs is the purest form of laughter because it is not for any reason and is not directed at others. Therefore, liberate your laughter and happiness from reason by joining a Laughter Club. Conditional laughter which is provoked by some reason or situation has its expiry date. The joy remains till the euphoria of that particular reason is there. If you can liberate your laughter from reason and conditions of life, it will give you joy forever.

WISDOM BECOMES MANIFEST IN A GROUP

We have a wealth of eastern and western wisdom which, if practised, can help us to lead a happy and blissful life. One may acquire knowledge about swimming after reading a number of books, but all remains good for nothing if one does not get into the water and starts to swim. This is the problem with most of us, that the knowledge about so many good things in life is not manifested for lack of motivation. We know the theory but we do not put it into practise.

In Laughter Clubs, without bothering much about the theoretical aspect, one can straight away start to laugh. As and when one gets into the process of laughing, one starts discovering the various logics. It is like a village lad who learns the art of swimming after he finds himself in the water. Looking back, the success of Laughter Clubs is attributed to a group effort. We know so many good things in life, but we don't get motivation to practise them. But if we do it in a group, it happens in a much easier way. Nobody would have thought one could laugh without jokes. It happened only when we all ventured into trying laughter as a group effort. In a group the motivation levels are very high. You don't have to do it, it just happens. You will do it because others are doing it. If we can laugh together, we can also practise ways and means of sensible living together.

LAUGHTER SUITS ALL AND IS USER FRIENDLY

Laughter exercise is short and sweet which can be conveniently added to your existing fitness programmes. It will be a value addition at yoga groups, aerobic centres, meditation centres, health clubs, sports and fun activities. You may not have to take special time out to laugh. The only requirement is that it should be practised in a group and on a daily basis if possible. Most important is that it does not depend upon external factors but your own internal resources. Whenever, wherever the group decides to, they can laugh and gain the benefits. If you are a working person, group laughter will give you instant relaxation and help you to increase well being, so that you can work hard throughout the day. If you are the kind of person who needs to socialise and increase social contacts and become a part of a support group, it has social medicine in it. This kind of format is ideally suited for retired people and the elderly.

If you are a person with intelligent introspection and a spiritual inclination, it has a lot of philosophy in it. You can learn the art of living through laughter. In a nutshell, the concept of Laughter Clubs has something for everyone to learn and get benefits.

WORLD PEACE: THE MANTRA FOR THE NEW MILLENNIUM

There is a war in the world because we are at war within ourselves. If we can bring peace inside us there will be peace outside. If we can bring peace inside us by practising yogic laughter and following ways and

18

means of sensible living and these Laughter Clubs multiply all over the world, there will be everlasting peace on this planet.

I have seen this magic already happening in Laughter Clubs: All the members of various Laughter Clubs have become like a "Laughing Family". Our mission is to set up Laughter Clubs all over the world because laughter is a powerful emotion and can bring countries together. Laughter has no language barriers, it knows no boundaries and does not discriminate between caste, creed and colour. Most importantly, it is common to all religions and this is the new religion which has the potential to bind humanity together and lead to a unified world, which is my ultimate dream.

CHAPTER - 2

Why Do We Need to Laugh More Today?

Today, life is very stressful and stress-related diseases are on the rise. More than 70% of illnesses have some relation to stress. High blood pressure, heart disease, anxiety, depression, frequent coughs and colds, nervous breakdowns, peptic ulcers, insomnia, allergies, asthma, irritable bowel syndrome, colitis, menstrual difficulties, migraine and even cancer have some relation to stress. To escape stress, people turn to alcohol, smoking and drugs. If you suffer from any of the following symptoms, you are probably heading for any of the above diseases or a combination of them.

❖ Nagging ache at the base of the neck

❖ Frequent headaches with tender temples

❖ Lethargy and constant fatigue

❖ Frequent coughs and colds

- ❖ Stomach knots
- ❖ Nausea and indigestion
- ❖ Irritable bowels or constipation
- ❖ Muscle tension with backache and neckache
- ❖ Altered sleep patterns e.g. difficulty in going to sleep, early waking.
- ❖ Breathlessness, bouts of dizziness, light-headedness
- ❖ Increase/decrease in eating
- ❖ Increased smoking or drinking
- ❖ Loss of sexual drive
- ❖ Frequent mood swings
- ❖ Feeling of isolation
- ❖ Lack of self-worth
- ❖ Frequent memory lapses
- ❖ Poor decision-making
- ❖ Irritability and aggression
- ❖ Difficulty in concentration and alloting priorities
- ❖ Suicidal tendency

All of us get some of the above symptoms off and on in this fast paced life. But, if the symptoms recur and persist for a long time, you need to unwind and become a member of a Laughter Club. People try a number of relaxation techniques like exercise, massage, yoga, meditation and going for holidays, picnics and outings. All these methods are time consuming and expensive. One needs concentration and will power to stick to these methods. Most exercise programmes are abandoned due to boredom and lack of motivation. Yogic laughter (*Hasya Yoga*) in a group is one of the easiest and most economical de-stressing measures. Not only do we laugh in a group, but we also practise and implement ways and means of sensible living. Due to the group effort, motivation levels are high and there is no boredom, it being a short and sweet exercise.

FOOLISH PLEASURES

Everybody is after making more money than they actually need. Those who already have it, want to make more. While poor people are struggling to make both ends meet, the middle and upper middle classes are finding it difficult to earn enough to keep pace with their expenses. Modern technology is flooding us with luxury items which are becoming necessities today. There is no sense of contentment and people are always worrying about what they don't have instead of enjoying what they have. Today we are using scientific knowledge to please our senses. All our achievements hinge on amassing luxuries and we all seem to be indulging in foolish pleasures instead of meeting the basic needs of graceful living.

COMPETITION - THE KILLER

We are always comparing ourselves with each other in terms of material achievements and worldly possessions. In the name of growth and development we are creating comforts and luxuries which are taking rich people away from nature. They are falling prey to a number of stress-related diseases, because of a sedentary life style. Moreover, the use of science and technology is making everything too expensive and beyond the reach of common people. They are being lured towards a life of luxury, to achieve which they keep on struggling throughout their lives.

All the perils of modern living have resulted from competition. While healthy competition is necessary for growth and development, it seems that today competition is unlimited. It makes us feel like losers even if we are winners. It puts a person at the top in stress for fear of losing his position. If someone overtakes you, it brings a sense of shame and depression and negative feelings of inferiority and jealousy. Due to this, people can't celebrate their small achievements and this leads to dissatisfaction and frustration, which in turn leads to drug addition, alcoholism, gambling, violence and corruption. In a collective effort to understand life in a better way and live more joyfully we have created the platform of Laughter Cubs, where like-minded people will together resolve to live a value-based life, rather than running a perpetual rat race.

ECONOMIC RECESSION

Today there is a terrible economic recession all over the world. So called sound economies are facing a dead end. Production capacities are large and the buying capability is decreasing day by day. Business houses have set such high growth rates that they feel like losers even when they are earning more than previous years. Even sound economies, like that of Japan, are collapsing. The leaders in electronics and automobiles are reeling under bad recessions even though the Japanese are known to be the hardest working people in the world. With global recession setting in, one thing is very clear, that in the days to come expenses are going to rise much more than income. All that we can do easily is to cut down our needs and start enjoying what we have rather than borrowing money to set high standards. This is very much a part of our agenda in Laughter Clubs, in addition to laughing in a yogic way for relaxation.

OVERSERIOUSNESS

The whole world is full of seriousness. As a child, one is asked by one's parents over and again, "When will you become serious?" As an adult if you want to be joyful at times, people will say, "Don't behave like a child! Life is serious, death is serious." There is a lot of seriousness in hospitals and religious places. There is no laughter at work places. Newspapers and television programmes are continually bombarding us with bad news and negative thoughts, which make people even more insecure. At a tender age, children are being loaded with information. Instead of basket ball, they are playing computer games and chess, where you need to apply lot of thought and there is practically no laughter. Already children of today are behaving like young adults. People are becoming more logic-oriented. They look for logic in laughter too. The very essence of laughter is absurdity. Where there is logic, there is no laughter.

We are already paying a heavy price for taking life too seriously and now the time has come to take laughter seriously. We are trying to break the seriousness of life through Laughter Clubs and revive the spirit of laughter to bring it back as a way of life.

LAUGHING IS FORGOTTEN

Modern man has forgotten to laugh, says a report presented at an international congress on humour at Basel, Switzerland, in October 1998. Despite being more prosperous today, people are more miserable than their counterparts 40 years ago. According to a study, even in the years of economic depression in the 1950's, people laughed 18 minutes a day. But today we laugh not more than 6 minutes a day, despite huge rises in the standards of living. "Today people are ten times more likely to be depressed because they put a high premium on success and performance and when they fail to

24

reach these levels they are possessed with a sense of shame and depression," says a German Psychologist, Micheal Titze.

Due to overseriousness, our sense of humour is also getting sick. The things at which we used to laugh heartily 3 to 4 decades ago, no longer stimulate even the faintest smile. Real resounding laughter, the kind that makes a person roll over and slap his thighs, the kind that brings tears, is missing today. We hear stories of people watching comedy shows of Charlie Chaplein, the Marx Brothers, Laurel and Hardy and laughing uproariously, laughing to tears. That kind of laughter does not happen today.

We see children and adults watching the same movies today with hardly a smile, let alone laughter. We need very hilarious jokes to tickle us as compared to our counterparts 50 years ago who went wild with hilarity even on hearing reasonably funny jokes. It seems that stress has raised our laughter threshold. Maybe this is due to more education and knowledge. If you go to the countryside, people still have a very low laughter threshold. They can laugh even over small things. People from villages are able to maintain a smile whenever they talk to a man from the city, while *vice versa* this is not true.

LIVING ROBOTS

Living in this mechanical world it seems we have become like robots, working all the time to improve our mechanical advantage. Do you remember the last time you experienced laughter coming right from your heart and from your whole being? When was it that you laughed to tears and your sides started hurting you? Didn't you feel tension being washed away from your system? Yes! dear friends, it is very hard to remember when whole-hearted laughter last occured.

I have spoken to many comedians, humorists and mimicry artists and they also agree that there is a sharp decline in people's ability to laugh in big cities. They need much bigger stimuli now.

25

CONDITIONAL LAUGHTER AND HAPPINESS

Why can children laugh more than 300-400 times in a day and adults only 15 times? This is because children have not decided upon any conditions for their laughter. They laugh because they want to laugh and are joyful. As we grow, we start setting conditions for our laughter and happiness. If I get this, I laugh. Only if I get a job of my liking, am I happy. So on and so forth. We are therefore always looking for some reason to laugh. Today there are very few situations which really make us laugh, but there are hundreds of things which can make us unhappy. The Laughter Club is a joint effort of like-minded people to liberate laughter and happiness from reason. We all decide to be happy, irrespective of what happens in our lives.

EXPENSIVE MODERN MEDICINE

There is no substitute for modern medicine as it can save people from the very clutches of death. The results of surgery are unmatched. Life expectancy has increased significantly because of advanced medical, surgical and diagnostic techniques. However, despite research and development, the incidence of heart disease, blood pressure, allergic disorders, psychosomatic disorders and cancer is rising, obviously because of stress. For most people in developing countries, modern medical treatment is becoming expensive and beyond their reach. A major part of their income is being spent on treating stress-related diseases. A wonder medicine like laughter can save on medical expenses by strengthening the immune system, which plays a key role in preventing a large number of diseases.

WHY INDIANS DON'T SMILE

The concept of Laughter Clubs has originated in India, perhaps because we need to laugh the most. "Indians don't laugh and smile," observe most of my friends from overseas who come to visit our fascinating Laughter Clubs. Maybe it is not part of our culture. As a mark of respect, we are told not to laugh in front of elders. It is bad manners to laugh in a place where everyone is serious. Maybe Indians are suppressed because of the British rule of over two centuries and we paid a tough price for freedom. And now after 50 years of freedom there is hardly anything to laugh about.

A mounting budgetary deficit, IMF loans, rising prices, governments tumbling almost every year, general elections being held at the cost of honest tax payers, politicians hurling microphones to blast each other and trying hard to put each other behind bars, financial scams, falling stock markets, a Yo Yo rupee, exports dipping, industrial growth going down, gang-wars, killings, extortions, vegetable prices soaring in a vegetarian country, so much poverty, pollution, traffic jams, increasing slums, homeless people sleeping on the roads... still there are thousands of people all over the country who laugh their heads off first thing in the morning and each group is known as a Laughter Club. Already there are more than 300 such clubs, with many more to start. Isn't India a great country?

Human beings are the only species in the world who are blessed by the Almight with the ability to laugh. No other creature can laugh. Everyone knows laughter is an effective anti-stress measure. Maybe the Lord has given us this ability because He knew that poor man would create a lot of stress. Perhaps He has provided laughter as a 'Safety Valve'. Now we need to use this safety valve deliberately and often.

27

CHAPTER - 3

How did the Idea of Laughter Club Originate?

It was an American journalist Norman Cousins who shook the medical fraternity by discovering the healing powers of laughter. He was suffering from an incurable disease of the spine, ankylosing spondylities. He was crippled with pain and modern medical science failed to offer any relief. He experimented with the healing power of laughter by watching humorous films on video and his pain almost disappeared and his symptoms subsided. He published a book "Anatomy of an Illness" in 1978. After that, scientists all over the world discovered the effects of laughter on various systems of the body. Inspite of proven benefits, people do not laugh enough today. Life is becoming more and more complicated. Laughter was tried out by isolated groups of yoga enthusiasts from time to time. It was experimented as a form of meditation by Osho Rajneesh and all over the world people tried many methods of making people laugh.

Many books have been written on the therapeutic value of laughter. People have tried laughter as a therapy to control many diseases. There are many laughter clinics in the UK, USA and other countries in the west.

In March, 1995, I thought of writing an article on 'Laughter - the Best Medicine', when I found a large amount of scientific literature on the benefits of laughter on the human mind and body. But then I decided not to publish the article. Instead, I went to a public garden at Lokhandwala Complex, Andheri, in Mumbai and spoke to people about starting a Laughter Club.

So, on March 13, 1995, I motivated four people to start laughing, standing in one corner of the park. Initially, people laughed at the concept and ridiculed the idea. But when the health benefits were explained, many people got interested and the attendance started growing. The participants were mostly men aged forty plus, as well as some women and children.

In the beginning, all the participants stood in a circle and I would invite someone to come to the center and crack a joke or tell a humorous anecdote. People enjoyed the fun and felt nice after 10-20 minutes of laughter every morning. This method worked fine for about 15 days, after which the stock of good jokes ran out. Stale jokes, jokes targeted at a particular community, hurtful jokes and dirty jokes started coming in, which embarrassed many members, especially the women. It was evident that if we wanted to laugh every day we could not depend on someone telling jokes 365 days a year. Jokes were banned and it was decided that the club members would laugh without them.

HOW TO LAUGH WITHOUT JOKES

Most members found it difficult to laugh for no reason. After a lot of thinking and soul searching I came up with an action plan to help people laugh without jokes and did some basic research.

The biggest hurdles preventing one from laughing are inhibition and shyness. To remove these, the group members were told to gather in large numbers. The larger the group, the easier it is to laugh. Laughter initiated in a large group is contagious and people start laughing, looking at each others' faces.

Every member would raise his hands up towards the sky while laughing, which is an easier posture for laughing and makes one feel less inhibited. Each laughing session starts with a deep breathing exercise. Members stretch their hands upwards and take a deep breath, hold it for some time and then gradually exhale. This breathing exercise is similar to 'Pranayam' in Yoga, which helps in increasing the vital capacity of the lungs and helps in producing laughter. After deep breathing, everybody starts chanting Ho-Ho, Ha-Ha. Slowly increasing the speed of Ho-Ho, Ha-Ha, they suddenly burst into hearty laughter by stretching their hands up and looking at each others' faces. Each kind of laughter lasts for about 20-30 seconds. This Ho-Ho, Ha-Ha exercise is akin to a yogic exercise called 'Kaphalbhati' where there is a rhythmic movement of the diaphragm and abdominal muscles. It helps to facilitate the lungs in order to initiate laughter.

When a large number of people gather in a group and chant Ho-Ho, Ha-Ha, it charges the whole atmosphere with laughter. Since everyone can easily participate in this exercise, each one feels a sense of achievement. This was another step towards removing members' inhibitions.

LAUGHING AT THE SAME TIME

All the members were instructed to laugh at the same time, following the instructions of an anchor person who conducted the session. The anchor person gave his command 1..2...3. If all the members start laughing at the same time, the effect is good.

EYE CONTACT - THE KEY

While laughing, we discovered that if we look into the eyes of the neighbour and start laughing, something happens to other person and he too starts laughing. The participants are instructed to look at each others' faces, as everyone has a peculiar style of laughing. This helps to enhance the stimulus and generate natural laughter.

Over a period of 15 days, a few more types of laughter were created like laughing with the mouth wide open, no-sound laughing with lips closed and little humming sounds, medium laughter and cocktail laughter. To avoid boredom, a variety of stimulated laughter has been introduced, based on yoga. This also helped to promote playfulness among the participants. In a nutshell, it is not at all difficult to laugh without jokes if laughter is practised in a group.

CHAPTER - 4

Laughter Movement - the Happy-demic Spreads

The idea of group laughter for no reason is nothing new. It has been tried from time to time by various groups of people all over the world. I used to hear from my elders about yoga enthusiasts laughing out forcibly to give exercise to the facial muscles, throat, lungs and abdominal muscles, though there is nothing mentioned about laughter exercises in yogic texts. I also read about group laughter taking place in some countries as a form of therapy and about clowns performing to make sick people laugh and get well faster. Osho Rajneesh had created a beautiful meditation called "Mystic Rose" where one laughs out out for a few days followed by a few more days of crying and obeserving silence. Later I came to know about Robert Holden's laughter clinics in the UK and humour centres all over the world. But this was all confined to the four walls of a clinic, or a hospital where patients were made to laugh with the help of comedians, clowns, comedy films etc.

The novel idea of group laughter in the open, in a public place, by people with no specific health complaints was tried out for the first time on 13th March,1995, with just four persons, in a public park in Lokhandwala, a suburb of Mumbai (India). In a little over four years it has become a huge movement. My friend, Dr. Dale Anderson from USA has christened it a LAUGHTER HAPPY-DEMIC. At present there are 60 Laughter Clubs in Mumbai and more than 300 hundred all over India. The movement is now all set to cross international boundaries and become a global phenomenon. It is no more a laughing matter, though initially some felt that it was.

LAUGHTER MADE AVAILABLE TO THE COMMON MAN

The reasons behind the success of the movement are many. Never before in history has laughter been so well structured as to be indulged in by the common man in a public place, free of cost. This practice promotes instant relaxation and a number of other health benefits. The members belong to every section of society: doctors, engineers, chartered accountants, company executives, managing directors, middle class workers and retired people.

Going down memory lane, I recall how it all started with fun and I never dreamt it would become such a big movement. During the formative days it was quite difficult for me to get started. People were afraid of being laughed at if they joined the group. The first to object were a few representatives of the garden authorities. They thought it would be a public nuisance and noise pollution and advised me to discontinue. However, I persisted and I went around motivating people. It was after a few talks by me on the health benefits of laughter that people started coming forward. Still many ridiculed the idea and called us a "Band of Fools" or "Murakh Mandli" in our local language. There were about 200-300 people walking in that park every day but only 15-20 people joined initially. When they started enjoying a sense of well-being after the sessions, more and more people trickled in. This made the park authorities soften their stand and they allowed the group to go on with the activity. Soon, the number swelled to 55-60 including a few women. Initially, we laughed at jokes but that didn't work after some time. We learnt the art of laughing without jokes by inventing a variety of stimulated laughter.

PASSER-BY REACTIONS

The very idea of laughing in a public place without any reason sounded intriguing to many people who saw about 50 people engaged in what they perceived as a funny activity. Scores of people used to watch us from balconies of adjoining buildings and roadsides and the hundreds who walked inside the park couldn't resist staring as they passed us. The initial reaction of most of these people was amusement and surprise. The question in their minds was: How can they laugh in a public place without any reason? Some of those living around the park took half-hearted objection on the specious grounds of being woken up by the laughter. But that was largely for the psychological reason of opposition to anything new, even if it is for the better.

Among those watching from the road-side were youngsters who would watch the fun standing on the bridge nearby and respond with sounds of "Ho Ho Ha Ha" and then shy away from the scene. Many autorickshaw and taxi drivers who were not carrying any passengers would stop for a while and then proceed with shy smiles on their faces. Even bus drivers would slow down to get a glimpse of the laughing group.

The good thing was that it amused most. But there were a few who raised their eyebrows and thought we were wasting our energy and disturbing others. Some of them passed sarcastic remarks. It must be said to the credit of those who laughed that they took all this as as a part of the game.

34

A laughter session at Lokhandwala Complex, site of the first laughter club

There were a few people who would stand a couple of yards away and keep watching the proceedings without gaining the courage to join in. Many who wanted to join the group would hold themselves back, thinking that there might be some fees to be paid before joining. Efforts were always made to clarify this impression. Membership of a Laughter Club involved neither filling up of any form, nor payment of any fee, nor any other fuss. Those who were slow to get into the spirit of the laughter expressed the opinion that it was artificial or forced.

Those who practised daily found it beneficial and started to spread the news by word of mouth. Soon the concept caught on in the residential complex and many people would just come to watch these funny people in action. As we kept on updating our laughing techniques, people from adjoining localities also started coming and one fine day would express the desire to start similar clubs in their areas too. We were very happy to share the happiness. It was not more than two months from the start of the first Laughter Club that "Seven Bungalows", a nearby suburb of Mumbai, was resounding with the guffaws of the second Laughter Club.

MEDIA BREAKTHROUGH

The first media coverage of our Laughter Club was by India's most popular cultural show 'Surabhi' on the national television network. The production company has its office near the park where we had our laughter sessions every day. It tickled the curiosity of many newspapers and magazines all over the country. One fine day the news of Laughter Clubs hit the headlines of India's most popular English daily "The Times of India". The paper carried a picture of laughing members on the front page with a report saying, "This club is not a laughing matter". I was flooded with telephone calls and it created a flutter in the entire city. The effect was magical; our attendance went up by 50%. Requests from other areas started pouring in. Within 3 months there were 16 clubs! Lokhandwala Public Park became a famous hunting ground for journalists from various newspapers, magazines and national and international television networks. Our first international exposure was on BBC News followed by coverage on CNN and NHK (Japan). I have not seen such enthusiastic media coverage for any other social movement. Soon, I lost count of the frequency with which the laughter movement appeared in some national or international paper or magazine.

It did not take very long for the movement to spread outside Mumbai. In the month of July 1995, I was invited to Ahmedabad, the industrial city of Gujarat. I was amazed to see a crowd of 700 people gathered to witness the opening session. It was really a treat to watch so many people laugh, just laugh for no reason. How relaxed they looked!

The Laughter Club movement in Ahmedabad was spearheaded by Dr. Mukund Mehta, MD (Pathology), who was also a fitness enthusiast. He has been instrumental in setting up more than 28 clubs in Ahmedabad and many more in the neighbouring cities of Gandhinagar, Nadiad, Rajkot, Baroda, and Jalgaon.

A Laughter session in progress at Ahmedabad

Another philanthropist and laughter enthusiast Mr. L.N. Daga of Calcutta, started the first Laughter Club in Calcutta, with the help of Mr. A.P. Kumar of Ahmedabad. To date, he has established more than 50 clubs in Calcutta and West Bengal. Thanks to the media, and the enthusiasts like Dr. Mehta and Mr. Daga, Laughter Clubs have multiplied at a pretty fast pace. Now, we have Laughter Clubs in cities like Hyderabad, Pune, Nasik, Goa, Jodhpur, Udaipur, Kota and Jabalpur, and more than 200 request letters for Laughter Clubs to be started all over India and in foreign countries like USA, UK, Italy, Greece, Germany, Denmark, Swedan, Singapore etc. These are under consideration. To put it simply, the Laughter Club concept has turned into a big movement of happiness.

THE LAUGHTER MESSAGE GOES OVERSEAS

Some Indians settled abroad, while on a holiday to their homeland, were impressed by the idea and felt that it could be effective in terms of social interaction. They took video films and also got acquainted with the laughter techniques. They tried to establish Laughter Clubs in their places of residence, but their efforts did not make much headway because of, as I felt, inadequate follow-up. Still there is a great deal of interest in Laughter Clubs abroad due to the awareness created by the media. The *National Geographic* (May 1997 issue) carried a double spread picture along with the message of Laughter Clubs. This coverage was instrumental in spreading awareness of the concept all over the world because of the magazine's wide readership. The Laughter Club concept was discussed at the International Humour Conference in Basel (October 1998) and a small video clipping about Laughter Clubs was shown and a brief laughter session was conducted by a young laughter expert from Germany, Mr. Heinz Tobler, who frequently visits India. He had come to meet me and attended a couple of laughter sessions in Mumbai.

The *Los Angeles Times* covered the story of Laughter Clubs prominently. It seems to me that now there is increasing appreciation of the concept of 'Laughter Clubs' in U.S.A. Mr. Steve Wilson, America's popular joyologist and humour specialist, met me in Mumbai and was impressed by the idea. He felt that eastern and western wisdom about laughter and humour could be combined to make the world a better place to live in. As suggested by him, a tour which he has termed the world laughter tour, has been planned. It starts from Columbus (Ohio - USA) sometime in the end of May 1999. We will be visiting a few cities in the US to conduct seminars, workshops and Laughter Club demonstrations. A workshop in Oaklands (California) at the International Society of Humor Studies, on 1st July, 1999, is also planned. Mr. Steve Wilson has already presented the Laughter Club idea before the American Association of Therapeutic Humor (AATH), with a favourable response from participants. In October 1998, Peter Jennings' ABC News coverage about Laughter Clubs was highly appreciated all over the United States. An Australian television documentary "Run around the World" generated quite a bit of interest in Australia and I have received a couple of invitations from Sydney, Melbourne and Adelaide.

CHAPTER - 5

The Right Time and Place for Laughter Sessions

What is the right time to hold a laughter session? "Can I hold it in the evenings after I return from work?" "Must I go to a public park for my daily guffaws?" Can't I just laugh alone at home?" These are the common queries people ask, who want to be a part of laughter movement. You may laugh any time of the day, but to laugh in a group in a new yogic way, first you will have to join a group to gain the feel of the concept. Once you understand the concept and learn the various techniques then it may be possible to laugh with 2-3 people anywhere, or may be you can laugh alone at home, all by yourself. But to gain the maximum benefits, you must laugh in a group most of the time and in between you may try laughter with one or two people in a family. Laughter meditation which is described in this book can later be done alone.

IDEAL TIME

Ideally, a laughing session must take place in the morning, especially in India where weather conditions are very favourable for people to have a morning walk. Most Laughter Clubs are held at public parks where people enjoy their walks and have laughter sessions also. In northern India, the attendance becomes thin in winter, but still many who are regular walkers, like to continue their sessions in winter too. Most clubs have their sessions between 6 and 7 o'clock in the morning in open parks, according to the convenience of their participants. The total duration of deep breathing, laughter and stretching exercises should not exceed 15-20 minutes. Timing can be adjusted by a few minutes according to the suitability of particular groups and weather conditions if done in an open place. Why must one laugh in the morning? There are many reasons for this. It is always better to start the day with laughter. It keeps you in good spirits and in a good mood throughout the day.

It energises you and 15-20 minutes of laughter is carried throughout the day till you retire to bed. Though it is beneficial even if you laugh in the evenings, according to our experience, mornings are ideal. Because in the evening, everybody has his own time to come home and has other engagements. A few clubs were set up in the evening but they did not succeed because of irregular attendance, and people did not gain the same effect as thay did from morning sessions.

Secondly, a morning walk and a laughter therapy session are complimentary to each other. Both take place in a public place and hence it is ideal for walkers to have a session either at the begining or at the end of their walks. They can also have it in the middle of the walks. As a matter of fact, I attribute the success of the Laughter Club movement to the selection of the right group of people, the morning walkers. They are health conscious people who can easily form a Laughter Club to add to their health related activites. For those who come for a walk, laughter is a value addition to their exercise programme. Looking back, if I had not started this concept with the morning walker, it would have failed for want of regular attendance. Morning walkers don't have to take special time out for a laughter session. There are already in public places. Therefore, by making laughter a part of your morning walk, you make the session a part of your routine without the bother of specially finding a particular time for laughing.

Thus, the ritual become regular and you can get the benefits. Upon waking up the morning one's body is stiff. This is the right time to do stretching exercises. Some Laughter Clubs start with stretching exercises first, while people are still gathering. Most yoga lovers like to start with yogic postures at the time of sunrise. So the practice of *hasya yoga* or Laughter Therapy is started at about the same time. Pollution is least in the morning in big cities. During a laughter session at a public park in the open, you will get the freshest air you are likely to get throughout the day. This is an added benefit you get when laughing in the morning. By the time it is evening, people are so tired that they have no strength to smile, let alone laugh. Hence, laughing in the morning is the best thing to do.

In western countries, during winter it is not possible to laugh in the morning. Health clubs, yoga groups, sports groups, work places like factories and offices are the right places when people can gather first thing in the morning and laugh in a group.

CHAPTER - 6

What Happens During a Laughter Session?

In India, most Laughter Clubs start early in the morning when people go for walks between 6.30 and 7.30 a.m., depending upon the convenience of a particular group. In organisations, the laughter session starts according to the time of commencement of office hours. We recommend that people laugh before starting their work. Many factories begin with prayers and then laughter. The total duration of one session should not be more than 20 minutes, including laughter, deep breathing and stretching exercises.

The hallmark of most Laughter Clubs is punctuality. The anchor person starts the session on the dot of time, and people set their watches when the laughter begins. Since the session is only for 20 minutes nobody can afford to be late. People are seen rushing whenever the sounds of Ho-Ho Ha-Ha begin.

How Laughter Club Members Stand

All the members stand in a circle or semicircle, according to the space available, with the anchor person in the middle. He or she gives commands to initiate different types of laughter and exercises. The most important point to be noted here is that the members should not stand in a line to form a circle, as seen in military parades. The idea is that one should not feel conscious about breaking the circle or the line. It should be like a crowd format with people standing at random. The distance between members should not be more than 2-3 feet, the stretch of the arms, as members are supposed to look into each others' eyes and laugh. If the distance is more, the eye contact will not be effective enough to stimulate a person to laugh. Moreover, members should not stick to one place throughout the session. During each type of laughter, one should go up to different people and laugh with them with good sustained eye contact, or strike hands with each other whenever possible, depending upon the type of laughter.

A 20-minute session is a perfect blend of stimulated laughter, deep breathing and stretching exercises. One bout of laughter lasts for 30 seconds to 45 seconds. After each bout of laughter, or sometimes after two bouts, two deep breaths are taken, in order to give a break. This avoids exertion and tiredness. Sometimes, various neck, shoulder and arm stretching exercises are done in place of deep breathing between bouts of laughters.

Step I: Deep Breathing

The session starts when one takes a deep breath through the nostrils, simultaneously raising the arms up towards the sky, at an angle of 45 degrees from the middle of the body. The breathing in should be rhythmic, in accordance with movement of the arms and one should keep on filling air into the lungs, as much as possible, and then hold one's breath for 4 seconds. Then the breath is released slowly and rhythmically by bringing the stretched arms back to normal position. One can breathe out through the nose or preferably through the mouth by pursing the lips, as if whistling silently. By breathing out through the mouth like this, one can prolong the expiration, so as to also remove the residual air, which is normally held back in the lungs even after one exhales. Removing this residual air which contains more corbon dioxide, and replacing it with fresh air containing more oxygen increases the net supply of oxygen to the body. This is in accordance with yogic deep breathing (a type of *paranayama*) where the duration of exhalation is prolonged almost double the time of inhalation.

Deep breathing is a very valuable exercise for maintaining both physical and mental health. It increases the vital capacity of the lungs and keeps all the air cells operational to participate in the exchanges of gases. It also prevents bacterial infections in respiratory tracts, thereby being helpful to those suffering from asthma and bronchitis. Deep breathing cools down the mind and enhances mental stability.

STEP II: HO-HO HA-HA EXERCISE

All the members start chanting Ho-Ho Ha-Ha in unison, with rhythmic clapping 1-2, 1-2-3. (Ho-Ho; Ha-Ha-Ha). The sound should come from the naval, so as to feel the movement of abdominal muscles, while keep the mouth half open. While chanting Ho-Ho Ha-Ha, a smile should be maintained and the head and the body should swing forward and backward as if one is enjoying the exercise. This can go on for up to one minute.

STEP III: HEARTY LAUGHTER

After the Ho-Ho Ha-Ha exercise, the first kind of laughter is hearty laughter. To initiate all kinds of laughter the anchor person gives a command 1,2,3... and everybody start laughing at the same time. It builds up a good tempo and the effect is much better, rather than different members laughing with different timings. In a hearty laugh, one laughs by throwing the arms up and laughing heartily. One should not keep the arms stretched up all the time during a hearty laugh. Keep the arms up for a while and bring them down and again raise them up. At the end of a hearty laugh, the anchor person starts clapping and chanting Ho-Ho Ha-Ha 5-6 times. That marks the end of a particular kind of laughter. This is followed by two deep breaths.

STEP IV: GREETING LAUGHTER

Again under the command of the anchor person, the members come a little closer to each other and greet each other with a particular gesture, while laughing in a medium tone and maintaining eye contact. One can join both the hands (*Namaste* laughter), or *do Aadaab* Laughter by moving one hand closer to the face (as Muslims greet each other), or one can bend at the hips and laugh by looking in the eyes of the neighbour (Japanese way) or there could many other ways of greeting according to the region, state or country. This is followed by Ho-Ho Ha-Ha chanting and clapping 5-6 times and deep breathing twice.

STEP V: SILENT LAUGHTER WITH MOUTH WIDE OPEN

In this type of laughter, the mouth is opened as wide as possible and participants laugh looking at each others' faces and making different gestures showing their palms to each other, shaking their heads and sometimes their hands. Silent Laughter should be done with quick movements of the abdominal muscles as we do during spontaneous laughter. It should not be like a prolonged hissing sound, which looks more artificial.

Important: One should not apply excess force or over exert while laughing without sound. It can be harmful if intra-abdominal pressure is raised unnecessarily. One should try to impart more feeling rather than applying too much force.

45

STEP VI: HUMMING LAUGHTER WITH LIPS CLOSED

In this type of laughter, the lips are closed and a person tries to laugh while making a humming sound which resonates throughout the skull. People can keep on looking at each other, making some gestures to stimulate each other. Some people also call it pigeon laughter.

Caution: One should not try to laugh without sound while keeping the mouth closed with force. This raises undue pressure in the abdominal cavity that may be harmful.

STEP VII: MEDIUM LAUGHTER

In this type of laughter, one laughs gently in a medium tone while going up to another person, or strikes palms with each other, either above the head or below the chest or both. There is lot of movement in the group as one should try to laugh and meet 4-5 different persons. This is very enjoyable as it is gentle and can be prolonged a bit, Plus there is interaction between various members.

STEP VIII: SWINGING LAUGHTER

This is an interesting kind laughter as it has a lot of playfulness. All the member move outwards by two meters to widen the circle. On instruction from the anchor person people move forward by making a prolonged sound of Ae Ae- Aeeeee....., simultaneously raising the hands and they all burst into laughter while meeting in the center and waving their hands. After the bout of laughter, they move back to their original position. The second time they move forward by saying Oh- Ooooooo.. and burst into laughter. Similarly, the third and fourth times they make the sounds of Eh- Eh... E.... and Oh- Oh... O....... Many people are seen behaving like children and enjoying the fun.

STEP IX: ONE-METER LAUGHTER

This is the invention of a Laughter Club member dealing in cloth merchandise. It duplicates how we measure an imaginary one meter by moving one hand over the stretched arm of the other side and extending the shoulder. The hand is moved in three jerks by chanting Ae...., Ae....., Aeee..... and then participants burst into laughter by stretching both the arms. First the imaginary measurement is done on the left side and then on the right. This cycle is repeated twice. Again, this laughter has a playful quality. People enjoy the chanting of Ae... Ae.. in a staccato manner.

STEP X: LION LAUGHTER

This particular laughter has been derived from a yogic posture known as *Simha Mudra* (Lion Posture). In the lion posture, the tongue is fully extruded by opening the mouth wide, while eyes are kept wide open and hands are posed like the paws of a lion and the person roars like a lion. In Lion Laughter, the basic position remains the same as stated above. The only difference is that people laugh with the tongue fully extruded instead of roaring. Lion Laughter gives very good exercise to facial muscles, the tongue and throat. It is also supposed to be good for the healthy functioning of the thyroid gland.

STEP XI: ARGUMENT LAUGHTER

This laughter is competitive laughter between two groups separated by a gap. Two groups look at each other and start laughing by pointing the index finger at the members of the other group. Usually, the women are on one side and men on the other. This is also quite enjoyable and helps to convert forced laughter into spontaneous giggles.

STEP XII: DANCING LAUGHTER

Members are instructed by the anchor person to dance in the funniest way and laugh. This is very stimulating and enjoyable as many people come up with hilarious dance steps. All these types of laughter are intended to remove inhibitions and make a person more open and extrovert.

Step XIII: Musical Laughter

This is not exactly a type of laughter but a singing of Ho-Ho Ha-Ha-Ha in a chorus based on folk dances, popular songs or any rhythm like conducting an orchestra by chanting only Ho-Ho Ha-Ha. Occasionally some giggles are added to make it interesting. This laughter has many variations, depending upon the state and cultural group.

Step XIV: Gradient Laughter

This laughter is practised at the end of the session. All the members are asked to come closer to the anchor person. Gradient laughter starts with bringing smiles on faces and looking around at each other. Slowly, gentle giggles are added by the anchor person. Others follow and start giggling too. Slowly the intensity of laughter is increased further. And then the members gradually burst into hearty laughter. This goes on for about a minute. It is very refreshing and infectious.

Step XV: Closing Technique

At the end of the session three slogans are shouted. The anchor person delivers the first punchline by saying "We are the happiest people in the world." Everyone raises their arms and says. **Y-e-ee-s.** ''We are the healthiest people in the world!'' **Y-e-s.** "We are Laughter Club members!" **Y-e-e-s.**

Neck and Shoulder Exercises

Since there is some fatigue after completion of the first round, members need to take a break before starting the second round. Here, neck and shoulder exercises are done. They have been incorporated because cervical spondylosis, neck stiffness and frozen shoulder are common complaints after the age of forty.

Basic Guidelines for a Laughter Session

1. All the participants will start laughing at the same time when the anchor person gives the command 1,2...3.

Welcome to Juhu Beach Laughter Club Mumbai, Laughter session will start right here, Just wait for 2 minutes!!

Ho-Ho, Ha-Ha-Ha, is the warm up exercise along with clapping in a rhythm 1-2, 1-2-3. This is akin to *kapalbati & shaws shuddi* where there is rhythmic movement of diaphra and abdominal muscles while clapping stimulates acupressure points.

Medium laughter : Keep looking into the eyes of your neighbour and laugh gently.

During medium laughter you may strike hands with each other and laugh.

Greeting Laughter : (*Namastee* **Laughter)**
Join your hands and look into the eyes and laugh gently.

Another variety of greeting laughter is *Aadaab* **(Muslim style) raise**
your hands up and down by bending your head slightly.

"Hearty Laughter", stretch your arms out and try to laugh from the bottom of your hea¬. Go ¬ for 30-45 seconds ¬ followed by deep breath¬

Silent Laughter : Open your mouth a wide and laugh without making any sound. Looking at each other's face and making some gestures with the hands will make it more interesting.

Humming laughter : (Pigeon laughter) Can you please keep your mouth shut and laugh with little sound. Humming laughter is also known as head laugh because it vibrates your head. It is also a good chest physiotherapy.

Another variety of Ho-Ho Ha-Ha exercise can be done in small groups, by striking hands with each other

Take a deep breath while stretching your arms up in the sky, hold the breath for 3 seconds and release. Repeat five times.

Swinging Laughter : Spread out in a circle for about 2-3 meters and pick up laughter from the knee level by chanting Aeeee............... move towards centre.

Swinging Laughter : (First steps) Another view

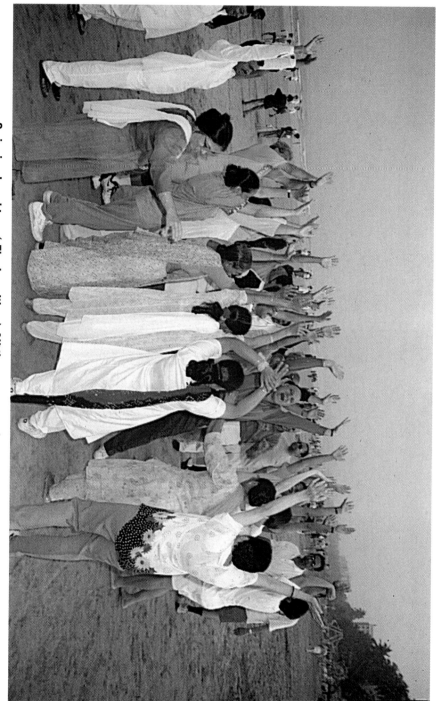

Swinging Laughter : (Final position) All the group members meet in the centre and laugh heartily by waving their arms.

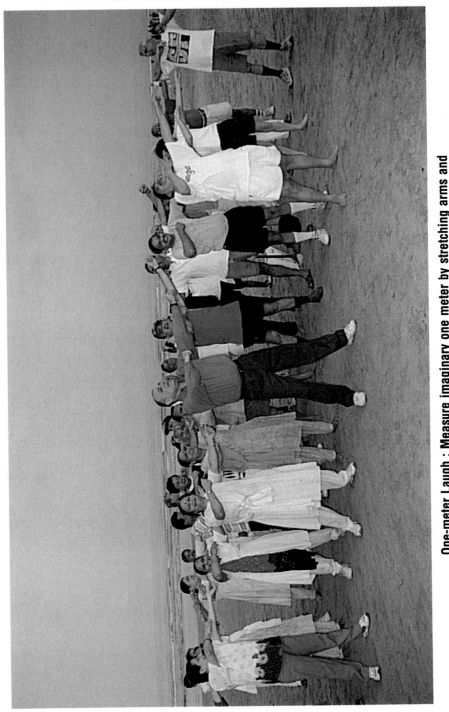

One-meter Laugh : Measure imaginary one meter by stretching arms and chanting Aee.......Aeee

One Meter Laugh : (Final Position)
Aee.......Aee.......Aee.......Ha Ha Ha Ha Ha

It's time for the break and do some neck exercises.
Stress causes neck muscles go into spasm and cause neck pain.

Shoulder exercise : Put your fingers on your both the shoulders and try to
draw "O" with your elbows. Many people got rid of frozen shoulders
after joining laughter club.

Lion Laughter : Stick your tongue out fully, pose your hand like paws of the lion. First roar like a lion and then laugh. It stretches your facial muscles, excellent for throat muscles and thyroid gland, moreover laughter comes right from your belly.

Lion Lady : Many women felt shy to take the tongue out in the begining but not anymore.

Child-like Laugh : She is only 85, and best at child-like laughter. No one can challenge her .

Child-like playfulness helps to remove inhibitions and laugh easily. You are welcome to dirive imaginary motorbike at no cost in laughter clubs.

**Argument Laughter : Why did you come all the way from Australia? Just for a laugh !!
Australian laughter lover sharing argument laugh with members of
Juhu Beach laughter club.**

**Argument with Ladies : Ladies are supposed to be the best at argument laughter.
If you don't believe, come to India and see yourself.**

Try laughter with your colleagues and subordinates at your work place life will never be the same. It will improve interpersonal relationship.

Talk something which nobody understands. Factory workers engaged in "Gibbrish" talk session during the laughter exercises.

2. People should not stand far away from each other. To laugh without jokes, eye contact is the key. During each type of laughter a person must maintain good eye contact with more than one of his neighbours.

3. Do not apply too much force while laughing, it should be more of a feeling and enjoying of the process.

4. One should try to feel free like a child and make funny gestures to make others laugh.

5. Any person who feels any discomfort in any part of the body, must get himself examined by a doctor and work out his physical fitness status before joining the laughter session.

6. A mildly heavy head, after a laughter session in the beginning, is normal. Such individuals must not overexert and laugh forcefully. If you are already a hypertensive patient, get your blood pressure checked at least once in ten days. Don't participate in laughter sessions if your blood pressure is high and uncontrolled. However, those taking treatment and keeping blood pressure within normal limits can join the sessions.

7. Any heart patient on treatment, or one who has had heart attack in the past must get clearance from his cardiologist before joining laughter sessions. Those with a history of heart attacks and those who have had bypass operations done, may join the session if their treadmill (stress test) results are within normal limits.

Standard Format for a Laughter Therapy Session

DURATION : 20 minutes (Maximum)

STEP - 1:   Clapping in a rhythm 1-2.........1-2-3
along with chanting of Ho-Ho........Ha-Ha-Ha
The sound should come from the naval and one
should feel the movements of the tummy in and out.
(Maximum 10-15 times)

STEP - 2 :   Deep Breathing with inhalation through the nose and
prolonged exhalation through the mouth and slight
bending at the end.   (5 times)

STEP - 3:   Shoulder, neck and stretching excercises
(5 times each)

STEP - 4:   Hearty Laughter - (Medium Tone) Laughter by
raising both the arms in the sky and looking at
each others' faces and then turning towards another
person in the group. (More emotion and less force,
followed by clapping 2 - 3 times and deep
breathing 2 times)

STEP - 5:   Namaste Laughter - Joining both the hands and
greeting at least 4-5 people in the group in
medium tone laughter (followed by clapping 2 - 3
times and deep breathing 2 times)

STEP - 6:   Silent laughter without sound - With mouth wide
open and asking each other - How are
you?......Fine......Very Fine....... (followed by
clapping 2 - 3 times and deep breathing 2 times)

STEP - 7:   Humming laughter with mouth closed - Laughter
with closed mouth, making gestures with the
hands and a humming sound (followed by clapping
2 - 3 times and deep breathing 2 times)

STEP - 8: Decent laughter or Medium laughter - Laughter in a medium tone by striking each others' hands above the head and below the chest and looking into the eyes of 4-5 participants (followed by clapping 2 - 3 times and deep breathing 2 times)

STEP - 9: Swinging Laughter - Starting with Ae.....Oo.....Ee.....Ooh the participant will bend slightly as if picking up the laughter and throwing it up in the sky by waving .bye.......bye..... (followed by clapping 2 - 3 times and deep breathing 2 times)

STEP -10: One Meter Laughter - Measuring 1 meter with both the arms and stretching out in three jerks Ae.....Ae.....Ae.....Ha-Ha-Ha (followed by clapping 2 - 3 times and deep breathing 2 times)

STEP -11: Dancing Laughter: Laughter with the funniest possible dancing gestures, while looking at each other (followed by clapping 2 - 3 times and deep breathing 2 times)

STEP -12: Lion Laughter - Extruding the tongue fully with eyes wide open and hands stretched out like the claws of a lion and laughing from the tummy (followed by clapping 2 - 3 times and deep breathing 2 times)

STEP -13: Gradient Laughter: Gradient laughter starts with bringing a smile on the face, slowly gentle giggles are added and the intensity of laughter is increased further. And then the members gradually burst into hearty laughter.

Last STEP: Shouting 3 Slogans: "I am the happiest person in this World" Y..........E.........S, "I am the healthiest person in this World" Y..........E........S, "I am a Laughter Club member " Y..........E........S

CHAPTER - 7

Exercise in Laughter Clubs

Most people living in cities lead sedentary lives. They use vehicles even for short distances. Sometimes I wonder when I see them waiting for more than five minutes for the lift to go to even the first or second floors. They expect their chauffeurs to drive the car right upto the doorstep. All this shows a lack of inclination to do exercise. This makes it difficult to stick to an exercise programme because one gets bored after sometime and abandons it. Being a physician, I treat a large number of patients for aches and pains, cervical spondylitis, backache and stiffness of joints, with a variety of pain killers. I am sure all these problems can be solved with regular exercise. I myself belong to an agricultural family. During my childhood in the countryside, I saw people working day and night, walking long distances in the fields. Rarely, did they complain of aches and pains. They ate a lot of saturated fats, milk and milk products yet the incidence of hypertension and coronary artery disease was very low. My grandmother must have swallowed tons of oil and she died at the age of 104. I believe they could maintain good health because of plenty of exercise which was a part of their routine.

The introduction of exercises (these are described in some detail a little later) and deep breathing in between the different kinds of laughter had the desired effect. A small percentage of people who had stiff necks and frozen shoulders, got rid of their painkillers. Some go to the extent of saying that the exercises have benefited them even more than laughter. And I have not heard anyone complaining of boredom, presumably because of the preceding or succeding laughter.

WALKING AND LAUGHING

Some have remarked that most Laughter Clubs seem to be located at places frequented by morning walkers. This is true. When I thought of starting Laughter Clubs. I could not think of a better place than a public park, where people go for a morning walk.

I thought morning walkers being health conscious would listen to anything conducive to good health. These are the people who are there everyday. One does not have to call them specially for a laugh. Looking back, it seems to me that selection of public parks for starting Laughter Cclubs was appropriate and contributed substantially to the success of the laughter movement. If in the formative days of Laughter Clubs, I had to invite people specially for a laughter session, I am not too sure many would have turned up with regularity. Morning walkers were already enjoying the benefits of their walks and they didn't mind experimenting with laughter. It was like a value addition to their morning walks. Walk and laugh, laugh and walk has turned out to be a perfect combination. With the introduction of Laughter Clubs, those who were not regular, started walking without missing a single day And, those who come merely for laughter, by and large, could not resist the combination.

EXERCISING FACIAL MUSCLES

There are very few exercises designed for facial muscles. Due to constant frowning the skin develops wrinkles. Different types of laughter help to tone up the facial muscles. Laughter also improves the blood supply to the facial skin and brings a glow to it. Stretching of facial muscles contracts tear sacs to pour tears into the eyes which form a thin film and reflection of light in this film results in a shining spot in the eyes.

OTHER EXERCISES

After the laughter session is over, many people who have time, do exercises of the eyes, yogic deep breathing and chant of *mantras* (religious hymns). Laughter groups have become very active and they have started organizing yoga camps, meditation courses, health talks, and acupressure training classes. This all has happened because they are able to share a common platform - the Laughter Club.

NECK EXERCISES

Today neck pain is a very common complaint. Because of stress, bad posture, soft beds or too many pillows, the muscles around the neck and shoulder go into spasm. Yoga gives a lot of importance to neck exercises, because all the major nerves and the spinal cord pass through the neck and control the whole body. Major blood vessels also pass through the neck and supply blood to the brain, which is the most important organ of the body.

Thus, the neck is like a bridge between the brain and the body. Everyday, in between various kinds of laughter the following neck exercises are done. By moving the neck towards right and left a pleasurable stretch is maintained for at least a few seconds. The neck is moved first from left to right and then up and down. People suffering from cervical spondylosis should not move the chin downwards. Instead, they should move up and then come to normal position. Lastly, the neck is rotated in a full circle, first from the left side and then right side.

Caution: Elderly people who feel giddy and uncomfortable while doing neck exercises, must refrain from these exercises and get themselves investigated by a qualified physician. Scores of people suffering from cervical spondylosis and neck pain have benefited from this exercise as they are able to maintain regularity by reason of exercising it in a group.

SHOULDER EXERCISE

Place your fingertips on both shoulders and point both the elbows straight and move them slowly in a circle from backwards to forward (anti-clockwise) five times and in reverse order (clockwise) five times. This exercise will ensure smooth movement of the shoulder joints. Due to a sedentary lifestyle, stress or diabetes, people after a certain age are prone to develop frozen shoulders. This exercise has both preventive and curative properties against frozen shoulder.

STRETCHING EXERCISES

Cross the fingers of both the hands, bend a little from your waist, lift both hands while taking a long deep breath, stretch both the arms above your head, reverse the palms, stretch your full body and bend a little backwards. This stretching exercise prevents stiffness of the body. It stretches the muscles of the front portion of your body, keeps the spinal cord straight and relaxes the muscles of the entire back portion of the body. It can be repeated 2-3 times.

The above three exercises are standard for every Laughter Club. There are a few optional exercises from among which, time permitting, a club can choose.

71

DURATION

The exercises during each laughter session should not exceed five to seven minutes, otherwise it will cut down the time for laughter. Exercises can be done at the beginning of the laughter session while members are gathering, or in-between various kinds of laughter to take a break, or in the middle of the session as per the convenience of each particular group.

LAUGH LIKE A SPANISH DANCER

CHAPTER - 8

Health Benefits of Laughter Therapy

It is a little more than four years since the first 'Laughter Club' was set up. There is a growing demand for opening such clubs at many more places in India and abroad. Almost everyday, more and more people are joining Laughter Clubs and are being benefited. One of the reasons for these benefits is of course that laughter puts the members in a positive frame of mind and gradually makes them positive thinkers. Various benefits derived by the members are mentioned in interviews with members and studies conducted on a small scale. People suffering from a variety of diseases have benefited in some way or the other. But we don't claim that long-standing ailments have been cured by laughter therapy. Laughter is more of a supplementary and preventive therapy. We are starting clinical research on it very soon. It will take a couple of years before we are in a position to publish some very authentic research data on laughter therapy.

Sense of Well Being

The one benefit almost everybody derives is a sense of well being. After 15 minutes of laughter in the morning, they feel fresh throughout the day. There is no medicine like laughter which gives you such an instant result. Many have found that they don't get irritated over trivial things and their approach towards life has changed positively.

Depression, anxiety and psychosomatic disorders

The stress and strain of modern life are taking a heavy toll of the human mind and body. Mind-related diseases like anxiety, depression, nervous breakdowns and sleeplessness are on the rise. Laughter has benefited many people who were on heavy tranquillizers and sleeping pills. Now they are getting better sleep and their depression has reduced. People with suicidal tendencies have started living with more hope.

Meditation and Relaxation

Laughter is one of the finest anti-stress measures. It is ideally suited for today's stress ridden lifestyle. It can be said to be a form of meditation or relaxation. For meditation, one has to put in a concerted effort to completely detach oneself, on mental and emotional levels, from one's own feelings and thought processes, as well as from the physical world to prevent distractions. On the other hand, while laughing, we do not have any conscious thought process and all our senses naturally and effortlessly combine in a moment of harmony, to give joy, peace and relaxation. In other types of meditation you need to concentrate a lot to take your mind away from distracting thoughts, which is easier said than done. Therefore, laughter is, if I may say so, the easiest form of meditation, which brings you instant relaxation.

High Blood Pressure and Heart Disease

There are a number of causes for high blood pressure and heart

disease like heredity, obesity, smoking and excessive intake of saturated fats. But stress is one of the major factors. Laughter definitely
helps to control blood pressure by reducing the release of stress
related hormones and bringing relaxation.

In experiments it has been proved that there is a drop of 10-20 mm.
pressure after participating for 10 minutes in a laughter session. It
does not mean that those who are taking 2-3 tablets for blood pressure everyday will be completely cured. Maybe, you will require 2
tablets if you are taking 3, or borderline high blood pressure patients may not require any medication after some time. It takes years
to develop high blood pressure. It cannot be reversed in a few days
or a month. But definitely laughter will exercise some control and
arrest further progress of the disease.

Similarly, if you are at high risk of developing heart disease, laughter could be the best preventive medicine. Those who are suffering
from heart disease and have stabilized on medication will find that
laughter improves the blood circulation and oxygen supply to the
heart muscles. Those who have had heart attacks or have undergone
bypass surgery can also participate in a Laughter Club's laughter
therapy.

STRENGTHENS THE IMMUNE SYSTEM

Our immune system plays a most important role in keeping good
health and keeping away infections, allergies and cancers. It has been
proved by psychoneuroimmunologists that all negative emotions like
anxiety, depression or anger weaken the immune system of the body,
thereby reducing its fighting capacity against infections. Laughter helps
to increase the count of natural killer lymphocytes (a type of white
cell) and also raises the antibody levels.

Researchers have found more antibodies in the mucous on of the
nose and respiratory passages after laughter therapy. There are many
members of Laughter Clubs who have noticed that the frequency of

Laughter session in progress at Saibaba Garden in Borivli, Mumbai

common colds, sore throats and chest infections has decreased. This is my personal experience also. I have suffered from very few attacks of flu ever since I have started Laughter Clubs.

NATURAL PAIN KILLER

Laughter increase the levels of endorphins in our bodies, which are natural pain killers. It may help in reducing the intensity of pain in those suffering from arthritis, spondylitis and muscular spasms of the body. Many women have reported a reduced frequency of migraine and tension headaches.

ALLEVIATES BRONCHITIS AND ASTHMA

Laughter is one of the best exercises for those suffering from asthma and bronchitis. It improves the lung capacity and oxygen levels in the blood. Doctors recommend chest physiotherapy to bring out mucous (phlegm) from the respiratory passages. Blowing forcefully into an instrument and blowing balloons is one of the common exercises given to asthmatics. Laughter does the same job, more easily and almost free of cost. There are many individuals suffering from asthma and bronchitis who are members of Laughter Clubs. They have reported a reduced frequency of their attacks. Laughter Therapy may cause some discomfort if you have severe bronchospasm. There is a small percentage of asthma cases who may get a little aggravation by doing any exercise (exercise induced asthma). Such individuals should consult their doctors before taking up Laughter Therapy.

One of the most common causes for frequent attacks of asthma is infection. Laughter Therapy increases the antibody levels in the mucous membranes of the respiratory passages, thereby reducing the frequency of chest infections. It also tones up the normal mucous clearing system of the bronchial tubes. Stress is another factor which can bring on an attack of asthma. By reducing stress, laughter can improve the prognosis of the disease.

IMPROVES STAMINA IN ATHLETES

Since breathing capacity is one of the factors which determines stamina in sports, laughter before any competitive sports activity will increase the relaxation levels and hence, performance. Laughter, I think, can be beneficially introduced as a regular exercise in any kind of sports activity.

INTERNAL JOGGING

There are plenty of exercises available for your body muscles, but laughing provides a good massage to all internal organs. It enhances their blood supply and increases their efficiency. It has been compared to magic fingers which reach into the interior of the abdomen and massage your organs. The best massage it gives is to the intestines. It improves the blood supply and helps the bowels to move properly.

GOOD FOR ACTORS AND SINGERS

Laughter Therapy can be very beneficial for singers and actors. Increased lung capacity and exercise of the diaphragm and abdominal muscles will help to gain a better control over speech. Another benefit would be enhanced self confidence and reduced stage fright due to an increase in the body's relaxation level, which results from laughter.

MAKES YOU LOOK YOUNGER

People do exercise for all the muscles of the body, but there is no regular exercise designed for facial muscles except in Yoga. Laughter is an excellent exercise for your facial muscles. It tones up the muscles of the face and improves facial expressions. When you laugh, your face becomes red due to an increase in blood supply which nourishes the facial skin and makes it glow. Laughing people look more cheerful and attractive. By squeezing the tear glands through laughter, it moistens the eyes adding a little sparkle to them. Laughter exercises the abdominal muscles and helps to improve muscle tone of those with pot bellies.

REDUCES SNORING

Snoring occurs as a result of lack of tone in the muscles of the soft palate. Laughter Therapy is very good for the muscles of the soft palate and throat. Some individuals have reported improvements. We have already started clinical studies on the effects of laughter on snoring.

INTERPERSONAL RELATIONSHIPS

Laughter brings people together and improves interpersonal relationships. All the members of a Laughter Club meet each other with open minds and they care for each other. You will get a chance to interact with a number of people with a positive frame of mind. Today, members of different Laughter Clubs are like family members. They know each other well, they share their griefs and sorrows. They share their joyful moments too, by meeting each other, going out for picnics etc. They organize health workshops, yoga camps and naturopathy seminars from time to time. People from various walks of life come together and greet each other with smiling faces.

SELF CONFIDENCE THROUGH LAUGHTER

When you are laughing in a group at a public place with your arms up towards the sky, it removes your inhibitions and over a period of time you become a more sociable, unreserved and outgoing person. Admittedly, some people are initially a bit reluctant to join the laughter group, in spite of a strong inclination towards doing so, for fear of appearing absurd to onlookers. However, this is a passing phase and the very decision to join a Laughter Club opens your mind. Gradually, it also adds to your self confidence. It will also help to develop your personality and leadership qualities.

In a Laughter Club, many members are encouraged to conduct sessions. People who were not able to speak a word in public, often become very good public speakers. The Laughter Club of Johnson Garden (Mulund) has produced more than thirty anchor persons. With the passage of time, you will observe a transformation in your personality. You develop a more positive attitude towards life. Minor setbacks or irritants in everyday life no longer cause a serious disturbance, and you learn to deal with them much more effectively.

CHAPTER - 9

For Whom is Laughter Therapy Unsuitable?

Ever since the inception of Laughter Clubs, there have been some people intrigued by the idea, but with a shade of doubt about its side or ill effects. This is especially so among cardiac patients and those who have undergone bypass surgery. Fortunately, there has not been even a single untoward incident in the history of the laughter movement. But, being a medical man, I am aware of the fact that people are instructed to force themselves to laugh and stimulate others to laugh. This involves some physical strain and a rise in intra-abdominal pressure. Some people, in order to get more benefits, become over enthusiastic and do forceful laughter by over straining themselves. While there are others who might have silent ailments with no obvious symptoms. It order to work out the various possibilities of side effects which might occur, I held discussions with a number of medical experts from various medical

and surgical specialities. Therefore, a list of ailments was worked out and patients with these ailments were advised caution and medical advice prior to joining in at a laughter session.

HERNIA

Hernia is a protusion of abdominal contents - various parts of the intestine mostly the small intestine - through the weakened wall of abdominal muscles. In those who have undergone any abdominal surgery, the site of the incision becomes the weakest point. With a repeated increase in intra-abdominal pressure one might get an incisional hernia. Another common type of hernia occurs at the groin. The abdominal contents can protrude through the inguinal canal and produce a swelling in the groin area while coughing, sneezing and laughing. Elderly people are more prone to this condition because of muscles weakened by advancing age. Those suffering from a long-standing cough due to asthma or chronic bronchitis, should be extra careful because they are more prone to developing hernia. People with an enlarged prostate, who have to strain a lot while passing urine and those with chronic constipation are also susceptible to hernia.

The abdominal contents can also get pushed into the scrotal sac and cause swelling of the scrotum. This is also a variety of inguinal hernia known as indirect inguinal hernia. Another common site of hernia is at the umbellicus (naval). Some people do get a small umbellical hernia during childhood which progresses later on and becomes bigger. If someone gets swelling on any part of the abdomen or discomfort while laughing, they must get themselves examined by a general surgeon. The more susceptible people are those who have a chronic cough, an enlarged prostate or chronic constipation.

If you have a hernia on one side, there is a possibility of developing it on the other side too. The best option is to have a periodic examination and not to apply undue force while laughing. At the same time, there is not need to be extra cautious or fearful about developing hernia. There are, in fact, more chances of herniation with coughing, sneezing and forceful expulsion in a constipated person than with laughter. I have not come across any persons who are enthusiastic laughers and have developed hernia. If diagnosed to be suffering from hernia, once surgical correction is done, one should be assessed by a surgeon for fitness before attending laughter therapy.

ADVANCED PILES (HAEMORRHOIDS)
Those suffering from piles with active bleeding, or are at a stage when piles protrude from the anus, should not join the laughter session, as these conditions may worsen with increase of intra-abdominal pressure. The patient may join a Laughter Club once surgical or other type of treatment is taken.

HEART DISEASES WITH CHEST PAIN
Another commonly asked question during my talks on laughter is: "What if some one dies while laughing?" What a death it would be!

I wish I could die laughing and be assured of a berth in heaven. In poetry, people pray to God to depart from this world laughing. But, I believe they are not talking of the literal meaning. My answer to such queries is, if one was to die or get a heart attack during a laughter session, they could as likely die laughing in their routine lives. I am getting too emotional. Yes, people suffering from anginal chest pain should not join laughter sessions, without consulting their physicians or preferably a cardiologist.

But heart patients who are doing well on medication and those who have had heart attacks in the past and record a Stress Test (treadmill test) within normal limits can join the session without any problem. Even those who have undergone bypass surgery can participate in laughter if their treadmill test results are fine. In a nutshell, if you are allowed to take a basic walk for 45 minutes, you can definitely join a laughter session. Avoid laughter therapy for at least three months after a heart attack or coronary artery bypass surgery.

RECENT SURGERY

To be on the safe side, one should not join a laughter session, within three months of any major operation, especially on the abdomen. In the later case, one must get a go-ahead from one's surgeon.

UTEROVAGINAL PROLAPSE

In some women, ligaments supporting the uterus become weak after the age of 40. Downward sagging of the uterus occurs, causing discomfort in the lower abdomen. One of the signs of such prolapse is involuntary passage of urine while coughing, sneezing and laughing. Such women should avoid laughter sessions until they are treated surgically.

PREGNANCY

In a small percentage of pregnant women, there is a possibility of abortion if there is a repeated rise in intra-abdominal pressure and they should avoid laughter sessions, till some conclusive data is available, after conducting research on the effects of laughter on pregnancy.

ATTACKS OF COLD AND FLU

Acute viral infections are highly contagious and if a person with such an infection laughs, he is likely to spread the infection by way of droplets in the air. People should stay away for about a week once they catch a cold. The good news is that regular laughter therapy increases the resistance of the upper respiratory mucous membrane and people are getting fewer coughs and colds, as shown by a recent survey done in the first phase of clinical research on Laughter Clubs.

RULING OUT TUBERCULOSIS

Tuberculosis is rampant in India and there is a possibility of spraying out bacteria while laughing in open cases of tuberculosis. Through the anchor persons, a vigil is kept on those participants who have a cough for more than 10 days. In such cases, a chest X-ray, sputum and bloods tests are recommended to rule out the possibility of tuberculosis. Fortunately, there has not been even a single case of tuberculosis among more than 20,000 Laughter Club members all over the country. But we can't take this for granted and proper medical supervision is a must. Keeping a handkerchief or tissue handy is highly recommended for those who are prone to getting phlegm while laughing, especially cases of chronic bronchitis, smokers or asthmatics.

EYE COMPLICATIONS

Any person with high intra-ocular pressure (glaucoma) with a history of rational or vitreous hemorrhage should take the opinion of an ophthalmologist before joining a Laughter Club.

ANY OTHER DISCOMFORT

Even members without any ailment who experience discomfort during a laughter session, should discontinue their session and consult a doctor. If there is no problem, probably there is something wrong with the laugher's technique. We are holding regular anchor person training programmes to improve upon the techniques of laughter therapy.

CONCLUSION

All the don'ts stated above should not scare a person and deprive him of the beneficial effects of this wonderful nature cure, but caution should be observed against any untoward effects of laughter. We are setting questionnaires for all Laughter Club members, to gather vital information about the physical health of the participants and screen vulnerable groups. We are also making periodical announcements and sending circulars to make people aware about various precautions that they must take while participating in laughter therapy.

CHAPTER - 10

Essential Link Between Yoga and Laughter

What do a simple emotion like laughter and an univer sally acclaimed form of exercise such as yoga have in common? Yoga has always been distinguished as a classic system of Hindu philosophy because of the marvels of bodily control instilled by its practice. Yoga produces an unique physiological balance in the human body by connecting body, mind and spirit. Laughter, on the other hand, is a cognitive, affective and behavioural response familiar to every one of us. Let us try to find similarities between the two.

The word "Yoga" arises from the Sanskrit root 'Yuj' means to get hold of, integrate, harmonize. It means getting hold of our lives, integrating all aspects of life, harmonizing our bodies with our minds, spirits and society. When I first thought about the idea of Laughter Clubs, it was only to have fun and laughter. I didn't have yoga in

my mind at all. Inspite of initial ridicule by people, I pursued the idea till most of the members in public parks accepted it as an enjoyable exercise. When jokes didn't work, we learnt to laugh without them. I thought of how to make all the members practice these laughter sessions everyday for 10-15 minutes because everybody felt nice after their morning guffaws. Morning walkers are obviously health conscious people and they would want to do it religiously. I have been a student of yoga and used to give health talks at one of the popular Yoga institutes in Mumbai. I thought, why not connect laughter exercise with yoga? For a few days I kept on thinking about different aspects of yoga and how they could be connected to laughter. I went through a couple of books on yoga and gained an insight – Why not deliberately structure all the laughter exercises on yoga?

DEEP BREATHING

Since the act of laughter depends upon our breathing apparatus, the lungs and respiratory muscles, I thought of starting each session with (*Pranayama*) deep breathing, which is an important part of yoga.

Deep breathing has a calming effect on the mind and provides more oxygen to body tissues. Secondly, I wanted to give some pauses in-between the bouts of laughter and I thought, Why not interperse the different types of laughter with deep breathing? This will definitely increase the vital capacity of the lungs and hence their capacity to laugh. Later on, I realized that deep breathing is one of the most important parts of laughter exercises. In the normal course, the common man has no patience to do yogic deep breathing which we made an integral part of a laughter session and thus it became a ritual.

Raising the Arms Up in the Sky

Normally yogic deep breathing is done slowly and rhythmically with concentration and perhaps visualization. But this was not possible in a group where most people were standing. To give a rhythm and slow tempo I told my fellow participants to raise both their arms up towards the sky, and at the same time breath slowly and deeply. After inspiration they were asked to hold the breath and stretch the arms for 4 seconds and then breathe out slowly through the mouth, as if whistling silently, while bringing the arms down.

The idea of breathing out through the mouth was to prolong the expiration, as in a variety of *Pranayama,* the expiration time is double the time of inspiration.

Scientifically speaking, even when one exhales completely, there is some amount of air left in the lungs, called residual air. This residual volume is more in those suffering from chronic bronchitis and asthma. There are more chances of bacterial infection and less exchange of oxygen if the residual volume is more. Prolonged expiration as in *Pranayama* and some dynamic breathing exercises helps to remove the residual air, which contains more carbon dioxide, and replace it with fresh air which contains more oxygen. This is how deep breathing and laughter help to increase the net supply of oxygen to the body for better functioning.

Ho-Ho, Ha-Ha Exercise

If one observes the process of laughter carefully, one will see that during the act of laughter there is a rhythmic movement of the diaphragm (the major respiratory muscle which separates the thoracic cavity from the abdominal cavity), abdominal muscles and intercostal muscles (between the ribs) which helps to expel the air from the lungs in rhythmic jerks which produces rhythmic vibrations from the vocal cords. Also, there is contraction of the throat, palate muscles and facial muscles. There are some dynamic yogic exercises called *Kapalbhati, Swash Shuddi* (cleaning of respiratory passages in forceful jerks of breathing) and *Bhastarika,* which involve similar rhythmic contraction of all the groups of muscles involved in laughter.

In my search for a method of how to laugh without any reason, when they were told to force themselves to laugh, many people found it difficult to laugh. Therefore, I introduced a warm-up exercise of laughter called Ho-Ho Ha-Ha. People would open their mouth and chant in unison this Ho-Ho Ha-Ha. By doing so, it helped remove inhibitions and there was a sense of participation by the members. The whole atmosphere got charged with laughter and many people would get stimulated and start smiling and giggling.

This Ho-Ho Ha-Ha exercise has some similarity with *Kapalbhati,* and *Swash Shuddi* (Respiratory passage cleaning with jerky movements of abdominal muscles). Later this Ho-Ho Ha-Ha exercise was supplemented with rhythmic clapping of the hands, which gave good stimulation to the acupressure points in the hand.

The Ho-Ho Ha-Ha exercise, along with clapping, is done at least 3-5 times at the end of each bout of laughter.

Deep Breathing with Arm Streching

While taking a deep breath in between the laughter techniques, the arms are stretched, which is similar to a yogic exercise known as *Talasana.* In addition, there are neck and shoulder exercises, designed to exercise the muscles of around the neck and shoulders which are tight because of the stress and strain of modern life.

LION LAUGHTER

Another type of laughter that is practised exclusively in laughter clubs, which is similar to *"Simha Mudra"* of yoga, is that of Lion laughter. Here, a person is supposed to laugh while fully extruding the tongue, keeping the eyes wide open and posing the hands like the paws of a lion. This is a direct adoption of the yogic lion pose.

This posture has proved to be good exercise for facial muscles, and beneficial for throat ailments. According to yoga experts, this also stimulates the thyroid gland. Often such kinds of laughter are embarrassing, especially for women in a social gathering. But the participants of Laughter Clubs get over such inhibitious gradually and hence this exercise provides its full benefits.

K.V. PATEL'S CONTRIBUTIONS

Though it was a common practice among yoga groups to laugh voluntarily, it was just for the fun. It wasn't at any stage a recognised yogic exercise, but it was always on the verge of becoming an entity. There is no mention of *Hasya Yoga* (laughter yoga) in any of the yogic texts. For the first time it was coined by Mr. K.V.Patel (78 years young) a lawyer by profession and owner of an Ayurvedic drug company at Mumbai. He called laughter a part of yoga because according to him, if laughter was practised with love, it could create a hormonious and integrated life. He established a *Hasya Yoga Kendra* (Laughter Yoga Centre), a social organisation were he used to motivate people to laugh more through his lectures. He recommended that one should isolate in a private place like bathroom, bedroom or any private room. Stand striaght, look into the mirror and guffaw(Ha-Ha-Ha) from the depth of the belly for three minutes. Practice this daily, you will find yourself in a better mood even if no jokes were to be cracked for the day.

CHAPTER - 11

Scientific Rational of Yoga & Laughter

All the organs of the body are made up of tissues. To keep these tissues in perfect health and organic vigour, there should be a constant supply of nourishment like proteins, carbohydrates, fats, salts, minerals and vitamins. These are derived from the food and drink one eats. Their supply depends upon the quality of food one takes and the power of digestion and absorption of the digestive system. To reach the nutrients all over the body, one's circulatory systems should be efficient. Therefore, the digestive and circulatory systems should be kept in good order for optimum health. Finally, when the nutrients reach all the tissues of the body, oxygen is required for the metabolism. To get more oxygen supply our respiratory system must be in perfect order.

TONING UP THE DIGESTIVE SYSTEM

According to principles of yoga, health and vigour of the body depend upon the quality and quantity of food. A lot of emphasis is given to selecting the right food. Since Laughter Club meetings are regular, a lot of awareness is being created about healthful food among the members. Eating of raw fruits, salads, vegetables and sprouts is being actively promoted in Laughter Clubs. Every morning it is a practice among many Laughter Club members to bring sprouts of various lentils. Sprouts are an excellent food containing large quantities of vitamins and are considered very healthful. Along with sprouts you will see cloves of raw garlic, basil leaves (a sacred Indian herb) and neem leaves (Margosa leaves) kept at the venues of Laughter Clubs. Since Laughter Club members meet everyday, through the network, members receive information on various aspects of healthy eating. We are proposing to strengthen this network and keep a panel of experts through the central body, the Laughter Club International. In a group, people get motivated to develop good eating habits.

Once you eat the right food, your digestive system should be in perfect order to get most of the nutrients from the food. All the principle organs of digestion like the stomach, intestines, liver and pancreas are situated in the abdominal cavity, supported by strong muscles from all sides. Nature has provided a gentle massage to all the digestive organs by the movement of abdominal muscles and diaphragm twenty-four hours a day during normal respiration. During inspiration the diaphragm pushes the abdominal organs downwards and forwards and at the same time relaxes the abdominal wall muscles. During exhalation, the abdominal muscles are contracted and they push all the organs of the abdominal cavity inwards and upwards. Thus, nature has provided an automatic and gentle massage to the digestive organs 16-20 times a minute (normal respiration rate).

But, if the abdominal muscles are weak and the muscles of the diaphragm are not exercised regularly they cannot provide an effective massage. Today, due to a sedentary life style and obesity, abdominal muscles lose their tone, as this leads to excessive fat deposits on the abdominal wall. As a result, the abdominal organs get displaced from their normal places and their blood supply also gets affected. It can result in dyspepsia and a variety of digestion problems. To ensure perfect health of the digestive system, the abdominal muscles should be strong and elastic. There are many yogic poses which make them strong and elastic and give excellent internal massage to the internal organs. For optimal performance, muscles should be contracted and stretched. Yoga *asanas* like *Bhunjagasana, Salabhasana* and *Dhanurasana* are some of the finest stretching excercises for the abdominal muscles. *Yoga-Mudra* and *Halasana* help to contract abdominal muscles. *Vakrasana* and *Ardha-Matsyendrasana* are excellent for side abdominal muscles.

There are two important yogic excercises *Uddiyana* and *Nauli* for internal massage: In *Uddiyana*, there is a verticle massage to the abdominal organs. A wave of contraction travels up and down in the abdominal muscle. Similarly, in *Nauli,* contractions travel from one side to the other, giving a lateral massage to the abdominal viscera. I admit that no other excercises of abdominal muscles can match the perfect yogic excercise to build the strength of abdominal muscles and give an internal massage.

In Laughter Clubs we have different varieties of belly laughs which can excercise all the abdominal muscles and the diaphragm simultaneously. In between the laughter, there are stretching excercises for abdominal muscles by raising the arms, taking a deep breath and bending backwards slightly. Scientists have called laughter 'internal jogging' or a 'Magic Finger' which goes right inside your tummy and gives an excellent massage to your internal organs.

Regular laughter excercise not only strengthen the abdominal muscles and give constant massage, but also holds the abdominal organs in their proper places to ensure proper digestion and absorption. I agree, laughter excercises are no match for standard yogic *asanas*, but they can be done regularly to give excellent results at no cost.

For a Strong Circulatory System

Once the food is digested properly and absorbed, the nutrients must reach each and every part of the body and the circulatory system is the transport system. All the nourishment is absorbed into the blood and processed a bit in the liver and passed on the central pumping system, the heart, to be pushed throughout the body through a network of blood vessels.

Similarly, the blood, after supplying the nutrients and collecting the wastes of metabolism should return to the heart and lungs for purification. The most important organ of circulation is the heart. By rythmic contraction and relaxation of the diaphragm and intercostal muscles, the resulting expansion and contraction of the lungs provide a good massage to the heart muscles. A constant change in intra-thoracic pressure while laughing helps to draw in venous blood returning from all the major venacavas of the upper and lower body. In a good bout of laughter, there is dilation of blood vessels all over the body giving a flushed apperance and feeling of warmth. Pulse rate and blood pressure rise as the circulation gets stimulated, before they settle down even below the original levels ten minutes after the cessation of Laughter Therapy. In a nutshell, laughter helps to tone up the circulatory system of the body.

For a Strong Respiratory System

Once all the elements of nourishment are carried to the tissues, the most important element which forms a part of many enzyme systems of metabolism is oxygen. The principle organs of respiration are the lungs. For effective supply of oxygen, so that the full breathing capacity of lungs may be utilised, the respiratory passages should be clear and muscles of respiration should be strong.

Yoga lays more emphasis on breathing excercises because they help to improve oxygen supply for optimal function. The life force energy *prana*, enters our body through breathing. Therefore, breathing is

94

the most important part of health building at the physical level, as it supplies oxygen. At the mental level it helps to calm down the mind and at the spiritual level the life force energy can be upgraded through various types of breathing excercise *(Pranayams)*.

I deliberately incorporated deep breathing excercises to proved a break in between two kinds of laughter. Normally, in general routine, nobody remembers deep breathing, but in a Laughter Club one becomes habituated to deep breathing as we are doing it at least 10-15 times during each laughter session.

Normally, a person at rest breathes 16-18 times a minute. During daily rituals it goes upto 25-30 times a minute. During heavy excercise and intense emotional pressure the breathing can go upto 30-40 times a minute. Individuals suffering from chronic bronchitis, bronchial asthma or cardiac failure have higher respiratory rates. During the stress and strain of daily life, breathing rates go up and it becomes shallow. As a few lung cells, due to lack of deep breathing, cease to participate in respiration, they have a tendency to collapse and become non-functional. The lung capacity (vital capacity) goes down and as a result the person feels breathless after a little exertion. Regular deep breathing, as practised in Laughter Clubs, keeps the lungs at their full breathing capacity and also helps in emotional calming down. If one wants to achieve higher spiritual levels one's breathing channel should be in perfect order.

RESIDUAL VOLUME

After the inspiration, when the air is exhausted, some amount of air is left within the lungs. That is known as residual air. This air contains more carbon dioxide and can only be removed by forced exhalation, or in a prolonged bout of laughter. There is a type of *Pranayam*, a breathing exercise where expiration is more prolonged than inspiration with the idea of removing as much air from the lungs as possible. In our laughter sessions, participants are advised to inhale through the nose and exhale through the mouth by making pursing gestures to prolong the expiration, so that the residual volume is replaced by fresh air, which contains more oxygen. Similarly, all the bouts of laughter are like prolonged exhalations with brief periods of inspiration. After 30-45 seconds of laughter, the laughter group is asked to relax and take two long deep brealths. This increases the net supply of oxygen to the body.

CLEARING RESPIRATORY PASSAGES

Laughter sessions, along with deep breathing, are like chest physiotherapy for those who are smokers and have problems of bronchitis and respiratory airway obstruction. The Ho-Ho Ha-Ha exercise is akin to yogic *kriya* like *kapalphati shwashuddi* and *bhastarika*, where exhalation is done in jerks with force. Many people feel that after a laughter session they keep on bringing out some mucous during the day, which makes their breathing clear. Laughter has also increased the local resistance in the throat and they thereby get fewer colds and tonsillitis. Various breathing excercise, along with Lion Laughter has helped to keep their respiratory passages more healthy.

EFFECTIVE REMOVAL OF WASTE PRODUCTS

Another condition which is important for maintaining health of the tissues is the effective removal of waste products from the body. Carbon dioxide is a by-product of metabolism and gets cleared from the system by deep breathing and a variety of stimulated laughter. The massage to the digestive tract provided by laughter exercises helps to maintain good bowel movements. Good tone of abdominal muscles also prevents constipation by promoting proper evacuation and bowel movements.

CHAPTER - 12

Is the Laughter in Laughter Clubs Real?

A s I have stated elsewhere, to start with we took the help of jokes and humorous ancedotes to make people laugh, but the major hurdle to this endeavour was that there was not a large enough stock of good jokes. Besides, not everyone found all the jokes funny and most of them were targeted at some community or gender. This used to hurt the sentiments of one or the other. All this was, indeed, disappointing. Some went to the extent of suggesting that the idea of a Laughter Club or group laughter may be given up completely. After some soul searching, it became clear to me that if people have to laugh everyday, the idea of some one making them laugh would not be workable. That meant laughter had to be self-induced and for no reason except to derive its many benefits. When I put this idea before the group, the reaction was that of total disbelief. They could not comprehend that something that they had

A laughter session in progress at Malad (East), Mumbai

never seen happening could be possible. I was of the view that, in a group, not all laugh for the same reason. Some laughed because others were laughing. This we all witness in a cinema hall. When the whole hall roars with laughter, it is not because all have understood the joke.

After some explanation and pursuation, the group agreed to give the idea of self induced laughter, laughter for no reason, a try and never regretted it. They were pleasantly surprised to see the good results that were turning out, gradually. Psychologists say that the human mind tends, initially, to resist any change even if it is for the better. Similarly, I think, anything new, particularly an idea such as that of laughing for no reason, draws cynicism. Many people, mostly from outside the group, expressed the opinion that laughter at the Laughter Clubs is artificial as against laughter arising from jokes etc. calling the latter natural. This artificial laughter they said, cannot possibly have any benefit. Since some people seem to be very struck with this thought, I propose to deal with it, at a little length, to put the matter in a proper perspective.

The dictionary meaning of the word natural is: pertaining to nature, or produced by or according to nature, or in-born. If we compare flowers grown in gardens or farms with those manufactured in factories, it is very clear why the former are natural and latter are artificial. However, the so-called natural laughter (arising from jokes etc.) is neither something that pertains to nature, nor is it produced by nature nor is it inborn. Rather, it results from some effort, such as narrating a joke or manual tickling or some gesticulation on the part of some person. Thus, it cannot possibly be said to be natural even though it is called so.

Just as the so-called natural laughter is really not natural, similarly, the laughter at the Laughter Clubs is not artificial, because it is neither hand-made nor factory-made.

God has given mankind the capacity to laugh which he has not given to any other species. This capacity is inborn as even a newly born baby is able to laugh. What is, therefore, natural is this capacity to laugh and not any kind of laugher. Had this natural capacity to laugh not been given to us by God, probably no laughter of any kind whatsoever would exist.

DIFFERENCE BETWEEN THE TWO LAUGHTERS

Though the laughter resulting from a joke etc. and the laughter at the Laughter Clubs are not identical, if we look at them a little more closely, we find that there are more similarities between the two than differences. The difference is in the initial stage of providing a stimulus and triggering off laugher. In one case, a stimulus is provided and laughter is triggered, not by nature, but by something done by a person other than the laugher; in the other, it is by the laugher himself. Being convinced of the many benefits of laughter, a member of a Laughter Club goes there to derive those benefits. With that stimulus and motivation, triggering of laughter is not at all difficult. The reason is simple.

Mr. Paul Ekman and Mr. Robert Levenson, psychologists from the Univerity of California, have come to the conclusion that the advice, "Put on a happy face" may actually be beneficial. Their research has shown that facial expressions are not only reactions to emotional states but can provoke these states as well. The latter is what happens at the Laughter Clubs.

After the efforts to trigger laughter, in one case made by another person and by the laugher himself in the other, the resulting laughter, in both cases, is triggered within and also comes from within the laugher. There is nothing to show that the source of laughter in the two cases is different. Dealing with the question of source of laughter, Dr. Robert Holden, who conducts laughter clinics in UK and has written the well known book "Laughter - the Best Medicine" says in that book: "The answer is elusive. Even if we could ask the Gods where laughter comes from, they would probably just laugh."

There is one more similarity between the so-called natural laughter or the laughter resulting from jokes etc. and the laughter at the 'Laughter Clubs'. Both arise from the same capacity – the capacity to laugh given to mankind by God. In the case of a natural flower and an artificial flower, however, the two arise from different capacities. In one case, it is the natural capacity of seed to get converted into a flower. In the other, it is either, the capacity of the machine or the skill of the workman to make the flower.

QUALITY OF LAUGHTER

At times, it is contended that the quality of laughter in the two cases is different, and, one is more pleasurable than the other. This is also only an impression, and, of course, a wrong one.

The source of laughter in all cases, being the same, what I think is meant by quality, is the intensity of laughter. That, as also the pleasure drawn, cannot possibly depend on who or what triggers the laughter but, rather the reaction, i.e. how hearty the laughter is, whatever may be the type of laughter. The above is evidenced by the fact that all persons who hear a joke are not amused by it equally, and therefore, do not laugh with the same intensity. Some laugh heartily, others just smile and some are totally unmoved as they find the joke not at all funny. It is also true that some members of a Laughter Club laugh more heartily than others. That difference could be due to mood, level of commitment etc.

TYPES OF LAUGHTER

Coming to the question: Of what type is the laughter at a Laughter Club? There are various types of laughter such as smiles, hearty laughter, belly laughter, giggles, chortles, chuckles, hoots, cackles, sniggers and guffaws. In his book, Dr. Holden mentions, among others, simulated smiles and transcendental chuckling, and describes these two types as follows:-

SIMULATED SMILES

"Simulated smiling is a joyful version of the popular coping strategy known as "acting as if", that is, if you want to feel happy, act happy. Don't suppress your sadness; just feel the sadness and act happy anyway. A full session of simulated smiling can last anywhere from three seconds to three minutes. You may even, if you wish, add 'ha, ha, ha' and maybe even move on to more orchestrated and elaborate guffaws. Simulated smiles often stimulate the real thing."

TRANSCENDENTAL CHUCKLING

"This is the silliest of all the creative growth games that we play at the laughter clinic. To perfom transcendental chuckling you should, on waking each morning, sit in a cross-legged upright position before a mirror and embark upon two minutes of laughing for no reason whatsover. Life will never be the same.

Anyone who sends a tape of his or her two minutes of unconditional laughter to the laughter clinic receives a certificate of membership to the "Happy Human Being Club."

The aim is to achieve an expression of pure, unblocked joviality that will set you up for a day of joy. To perform this exercise you have to transcend and laugh through some of the self criticism, seriousness and unhappy belief systems that so often get in the way of pure spontaneous joy."

The laughter at the Laughter Clubs could be said to be both, simulated smiles and transcendental chuckling, but, I think, it is more of the latter. As will be noted, this laugher can be as joyful as any if certain things are transcended, and one of the things to be transcended in my view, is the impression or the belief that this laughter is not natural and, therefore, can not result in any benefit.

The pleasure and the benefits a person derives from laughter do not depend on the name of the laughter but on the extent to which he enjoys it. Therefore, if the above thought of the laughter at the Laughter Clubs being artificial is withholding any one from becoming a Laughter Club member and deriving the benefits of laughter, my request to him is, please leave that doubt aside and walk up to the nearest Laughter Club without any further delay. You will not regret it, and in the words of Dr. Holden, life will not be the same again. Even if you do not enjoy the experience or do not enjoy it much, as you will find from what is stated below, enjoyment will come, and till that happens, there will still be benefits, because scientists have found that even false laughter has benefits.

Research by Mr. Paul Ekman and Mr. Robert Levenson has shown that motions create emotions and emotions create motions. Even if you act like a happy man, over a period of time you become one. For a person to act happy is little difficult (not impossible), but it becomes far easier to act out happiness in a group. This is what exactly happens in our Laughter Clubs. We all are acting happy and the chemistry is changing to happiness according to Dr. Dale Anderson (from Minnesota, USA), who visited our clubs and found a lot of sense in the laughter at the Laughter Clubs. In fact, we acquired one slogan from him which is getting popular in Laughter Clubs which is, FAKE IT, FAKE IT... till you MAKE IT. Act chemistry, act chemistry and the chemistry becomes real. Thank you, Dr. Dale for a beautiful thought.

THE DUCHENNE SMILE

Although Norman Cousin's book "Anatomy of an Illness" on curing oneself with laughter was a layman's view point, scientific research too shows that smiles and laughter actually trigger pleasure centers in the brain, even if artificially induced. Dr. Paul Ekman has opined that we don't yet know what specific parts of the brain are involved in each emotion but we are gathering fundamental knowledge and showing that there is a brain pathway that allows you to generate your own emotions. Dr. Ekman has identified 18 different kinds of smiles, each of which uses slightly different muscles or groups of muscles. He found that a bored smile, a cynical smile, or smiling at someone's humiliation will do nothing to raise your spirits.

There is only one smile which activates the brain center for happiness and that is 'Duchenne Smile', named after Guillamume Benjamin Amad Duchenne, a French neurologist who experimented with and studied the muscles of the face when engaged in smiling. He discovered that when lips part and turn up, the eyes crinkle up showing crows feet, the upper lip droops slightly, then there is heightened activity in the left anterior region of the cortex of our brain, which is the center for happy emotions. Even an induced smile can turn your gloominess into an upbeat mood. Here I would like to quote the work of Dr. Dale Anderson, M.D. of the ACT NOW project based in Minnesota USA. He has a beautiful exercise in his workshops, where he tells all the participants to hold a pen between their teeth and write a few words on a piece of paper. Because the facial expressions of holding a pen between the teeth resemble a smile or a wide grin, it produces happy chemicals in the brain and the mood changes. Similarly, when the same exercise is performed by holding the pen between the lips the facial expression resemble that of sadness, one feels low after some time.

BALAMCHALANA

There is a *Kriya* in the science of Yoga known as *Balamchalana*, in which one lies on the floor and begins to roll about and laugh for no reason. Another example of artificially induced laughter which turns into the real thing with practice.

Dr. Col. K.L. Chopra, father of world famous Dr. Deepak Chopra, writes in his book, *Life in Your Hands* about the yogic practice of intentional group laughter which was rarely seen before Laughter Clubs came into existence. I used to hear about isolated groups and some individuals who laughed loudly for a few minutes. This artificially induced laughter, according to psychotherapist Annnette Goodheart, is interpreted by the body as real and as a result, the brain induces a flow of happy molecules, which flood trillions of cells all over the body stabilising the hormonal system and enhancing immunity. Instead of isolated laughter practice, here are the Laughter Clubs where different kinds of stimulated laughter based on yoga are spreading all over the world.

VALUE ADDITIONS ALONG WITH LAUGHTER

Even if you regard laughter as a mere exercise, it tones up your facial muscles. People do a number of exercises for all the muscles of the body but there are very few exercises designed for facial muscles. Voluntary laughter is an excellent exercise for your face. It brings a happy glow to your face and makes your eyes shine with a thin film of tears which are squeezed from the lacrimal sacs during the act of laughter. Deep breathing is an integral part of Laughter Clubs. According to the science of yoga, life energy (*prana*) flows through the breath. By controlled and deep breathing we can enhance our own well being. With the 20-25 minute package offered by the Laughter Club, you will carry home a beautiful habit of deep breathing at least 10-20 times in day. This helps to increase the lung capacity, thus enhancing oxygen supply to the body.

One set of stretching exercises relaxes the muscles of the neck and shoulders, which become painful due to the stress and strain of modern life. According to yoga, the neck is like a bridge between the brain and the rest of your body. All the important nerves, spinal cord and blood vessels pass through the neck. Neck and shoulder and back muscles need to be in proper tone to maintain the free movement of the neck. Along with laughter, we do a lot of rhythmic clapping with out stretched hands. This also adds to well being by stimulating acupressure points on the palms.

If you are not able to generate natural laughter, the simple chanting of Ho Ho Ha Ha will help to tone up your abdominal muscles. It gives an excellent internal massage to the digestive tract and enhances blood supply to important internal organs like the liver, spleen, pancreas, kidneys and adrenal glands.

You get an opportunity to meet with like minded people, go for outings, celebrate birthdays, attend health seminars and workshops and participate in national and international events focussed on laughter and happiness. You will also establish your contacts with laughter lovers all over the world and may get an opportunity to visit other cities and countries on behalf of Laughter Clubs.

Talking about enjoying laughter at the Laughter Clubs, meet Mr. P.T. Hinduja (75 years young), winner of the 'best laughing man' comptetition twice, once in 1996 among the members of the various Laughter Clubs of Bombay and again, in September 1998, at the All India Laughter Convention held in Goa. He was declared the winner, because both times the judges found him to be enjoying his laughter the most. Some one asked him "How do you manage to enjoy your laughter? He replied. "When I found that I was not enjoying the laughter very much, a little introspection told me that it was I, my own self, who was preventing me from enjoying it, no one else. I then decided that I am going to enjoy my laughter at the Laughter Club to the maximum extent possible and thus derive the maximum benefits.'' That determination and a little action did the trick and put the principle "motions create emotions as much as emotions create motions" into action.

LAUGH LIKE AN EGYPTIAN

CHAPTER - 13

How Do You Convert Forced Laughter into Genuine Giggles?

If you happen to see any laughter group forcing their laughter, without any fun and pleasure, don't frown. It still has benefits and remember that with all the benefits of acting happy are value additions like deep breathing and stretching exercises based on yoga. If you find that a particular group's quality of laughter is not very amusing, perhaps they might not have been trained properly. There are many ways we can transform our stimulated laughter into intermittent spontaneity. Here are a few techniques: 1. Good eye contact 2. Theory of stupidity 3. Playfulness and fun 4. Child-like actions 5. Gibberish talk.

EYE CONTACT IS THE KEY

Want to see the magic? Select someone close to you and look into the eyes of that person. Start smiling slowly and then giggle a bit. You will see that the other person will start laughing without even knowing why you laughed. It is because of the infectiousness of laughter and the absurdity of the situation. This a the most important factor we apply in Laughter Clubs to initiate laughter. Eye contact, effectively applied, is enough to generate laughter. People who are too shy to have eye contact lack self-confidence. Therefore, learning to have good eye contact during a laughter session will also enhance your self-confidence. This self-confidence will be projected into your personal life as well as in business. The spontaneity of laughter in Laughter Clubs will depend upon the effective use of eye contact with other members of the group.

THEORY OF STUPIDITY AND SILLINESS

People who really understand the philosophy of laughing without reason can laugh without any problem. But today, everyone needs to be convinced and wants a logical answer. If you find it hard to get into the spiritual depths of laughter, then think in the most simple way. This is known as the "Theory of Stupidity. At the outset, the very name "Laughter Club" is amusing to many people and makes them laugh silently in their hearts. The onlookers in public parks can't help laughing when they see a group of gigglers laughing for no reason. On the face of it, it is the absurdity or stupidity which makes then laugh. The idea of a Laughter Club makes then laugh. Laughter Club members laugh for the enlightenment and health benefits they get, but onlookers laugh at their stupidity. Whatever it is, the idea is ongoing and mind-tickling and sufficiently absurd-sounding to attract people. They then find plenty of reasons to become regular members. I have interviewed many people who swear by their health that the Laughter Club has changed their lives, but initially they thought that it was foolish and laughed at its stupidity.

This theory can even help one to laugh at poor and already heard jokes. Someone asked me, ''How can I laugh at a joke which I have already heard?" I said, "Why not? Another reason for you to laugh it that you already know the joke which is being told to you by someone with great effort and you may start laughing in your mind even before the punch line is delivered''. Believe me, I have laughed at many sick and poor jokes because of this theory of stupidity. This will happen only if you look into the person's face closely while he is telling a joke which you already know.

Another effective reason to laugh at a poor joke is that it is good for my health if I laugh. A Laughter Club member can easily laugh at anything because he practices every day. Another possibility is, if you already know a joke don't worry. The style of relating it might be more amusing if you watch carefully. You may enjoy the joke in a better way than when you heard it earlier. While you are participating in a Laughter Club, if you happen to make eye contact with someone who is laughing for no reason and in a funny way, it becomes a reason for you to laugh. One member may think that other members are stupid.

Another application of this theory is that if you want to laugh alone, looking into the mirror, try to imitate the laughter of some one you know, may be a movie character, Say Ha Ha Ha Ha and continue this for some time. If you are not able to immitate properly you will feel silly. The moment one begins to feel stupid or silly, a genuine laughing sensation springs up, which is a great feeling and can be enjoyed as long as one allows the feeling of stupidity to persist.

SILLINESS OPENS PERCEPTION

There is lot to learn from the silliness in Laughter Clubs. A person who can laugh at himself without caring about the people who are watching him, is a person who can make his laughter real. In the beginning when we decided to abandon jokes and laugh for no reason, some people found it difficult to come out of their shells. To remove inhibitions we tried child-like actions like swivelling the tongue, talking gibberish and dancing in a funny way. Silliness really opened the doors of perception. Being silly is the first step towards freedom and creativity. The word silly is derived from *sealy*, which means blessed, happy and joyful. We all have been silly during our childhood and played with endless possibilities of nonsense, absurdity and silliness. In fact, all great inventors were snubbed as silly to begin with and the rest is a history. Silliness is the gateway for inventions and innovations. A serious person will never take a chance for he is always afraid of ridicule by others. He will hesitate to explore possibilities and will not always be ready for experimentation.

Lastly, silliness will help to develop egolessness in a person. A person who can laugh at himself will not have a bloated ego. The ego is the seat of many negative emotions like anger, jealousy and greed. We play silly games in Laughter Clubs and it is amazing to see creativity at its best when the members come up with funny ideas every now and then. Acting silly is one of the basic necessities of being a Laughter Club member. Once your inhibitions are removed, you will find yourself at your best.

PLAYFULNESS IN LAUGHTER CLUBS

There is a saying that we don't stop playing because we are old, but we grow old because we stop playing. Playfulness gives immense pleasure especially in a group. If you observe people playing games without stakes and gambling, you will always observe smiles and some laughter. Children laugh a lot while playing any game. Playfulness is restricted only to the school days. Play is abandoned as soon we enter college.

As adults, people become very serious and are sure that playing is only meant for children. And whenever adults play they play to kill time or starting gambling along with the game and it is rarely accompanied by smiles or laughter, while children always play for fun. In Laughter Clubs we have devised different types of stimulated laughter with a lot of playfulness. 'Swinging laughter', 'one meter laughter' and 'cocktail laughter' are some of the examples.

110

In Laughter Clubs we remind people over and again that no one is ever too old to play and that the spirit of play lives forever.

FUN GAMES IN LAUGHTER CLUBS

Keeping up with the playfulness we are developing many fun games. We play during picnics and also during our regular meetings. Many Laughter Club and thousands of members are engaged in creating new ideas and fun games which have tremendous potential to make people laugh. These fun games can make people laugh better than jokes. The most important thing is that the members actively participate and create laughter, rather than passively watch any humorous thing. Some of the fun games we play in laughter club meetings and picnics are:

Cola Drinking Competition:- We call 3-4 members from the group to participate in a cola drinking competition. Most people have no idea of what is funny about drinking a cola. Soon the suspense is broken and cola bottles are presented with baby nipples (teats) fixed on the bottle tops. The sight of the bottles makes everyone laugh. When participants start drinking the audience claps in rhythm to make it more hilarious. In our experience we have seen people laughing much more at this game than at any good joke.

Saree Tying Competition:- The *saree* is a common Indian dress for ladies. One needs to learn the skill of tying a graceful saree. We call out the names of two to three couples, where ladies are supposed to tie the saree around their spouses. Amidst clapping and chanting of Ho Ho Ha Ha and with music too, we witness the process of a man being draped in a saree, which looks very funny. After the job is accomplished, the dressed-up men are asked to stage a catwalk as is done at some fashion shows. This is also a very popular fun game which makes everyone laugh.

Drawing a Moustache:- In this game the husband is supposed to draw a moustache on his wife and two to three couples participate.

We had this game at our first All India Laughter Convention in Goa in Sept. 98, where 800 people participated in a moustache-drawing competition. Imagine the variety of funny faces on such a large scale. During the tea break people could not help laughing looking at each other. Ladies especially were very enthusiastic about this fun game.

Hammering the Husband:-Two couples are invited to participate and ladies are given air-filled plastic hammers which do not hurt. In a this game husbands are supposed to cry and ask for help or forgiveness while wives hammer them with full force. The wife who hits well and the husbands who cries well are the winners.

These are the examples of few fun games which are the result of creative efforts from Laughter Club members. Different games from all over the country are shared by the network of affiliated clubs with the central body, the Laughter Club International. Very soon we are planning to publish a list of fun games along with pictures and a step-by-step explanation. The Laughter Club Fun Games Directory will be published by the end of 1999 or early 2000. These fun games are a good substitute to beat the boredom bug, over-seriousness and depression. By playing these games people will come to believe that there are many other ways in which we can laugh and make others laugh.

Child-Like Actions in Laughter Clubs:- If you want to get rid of your dependence on jokes and still want to laugh, simply become childlike. In the initial stages of the genesis of Laughter Clubs when we found jokes could not make us laugh much, we forced ourself to laugh in a group. But many people found it mechanical and used to become a bit bored with the activity. Laughing in a group provides a stimulus while child-like behaviour by adults helps them to get over their inhibitions. We do lot of child-like actions in Laughter Clubs; like producing funny sounds by swivelling the tongue inside the mouth, tapping air-filled cheeks, laughing like a child and talking gibberish. We keep on reminding our members about the impor-

It's ALL FOOLS DAY - On 1st April 1999, more than 100 anchor persons from various laughter clubs of Mumbai, celebrated an event where everything was funny!!

Everybody was supposed to wear a "Mad Cap" and the chief guest was presented a bouquet made out of attractive yellow bananas.

Oh-my-my..., the cake is very hard to cut, why don't we try all together.

"Hey! How can eat a cake made out of thermocol". After cutting the cake with saw Mr. Jagdish Mehra offering a big piece to Mrs. Ranjanben of Jalgaon Laughter Club.

"Nice to meet you Sir, I thought this naturopathic garland would be best for your diabetes". Dr. Kataria honouring Mr. J.K. Kapur from Worli Laughter Club.

A fun game called "Hammering the husband" made everybody laugh like mad during Fool's day celebrations.

"Not bad at all! We feel very nice in a female-dress".
Mr. Roy and Mr. Chandwaney participating in saree draping competition.

tance of being like a child. Robert Holden is his book "Laughter the Best Medicine" says: "Every child is born with abundant creative potential for laughter, fun, play, happiness and love. Any restraint on any of these has an adverse effect on the child's growth and development. Anyone who grows with the inner child will find health, harmony and happiness. Therefore, instead of growing out of the child, we should grow with the child."

As adults, very few persons retain the excitement of a child. Poems have been written about one's desire to get back to one's childhood days. This alone is not enough. Some additional action is necessary. Just as one cannot learn swimming without getting into the water, one can be child-like only by behaving like one. In a given period of time every day we, all the Laughter Club members, try to revisit our childhood and try to carry that carefree spirit over to daily life. Child-like activities can be done either with one's own children/grand-children or in a group of adults at Laughter Clubs.

GIBBERISH GAME

Talking gibberish is one of the best methods to drain out stress. It is a very good catharsis. But in Laughter Clubs we use this as a tool to remove inhibitions and act like a child so as to create laughter. Nowadays it is being extensively used as a warm-up exercise in Laughter Clubs to open up. For the first time a gibbrish contest was held at the Goa convention where 35 people participated and made everyone laugh like mad.

CHAPTER - 14

Sensible Living: Paying Compliments - The Inner Laugh

S oon after Laughter Clubs started gaining momentum, the wife of a Laughter Club member telephoned me to complain that, while her husband laughed heartily every morning in his Laughter Club, at home he continued to shout at the family members, the same as he did earlier. Then she asked: Should not Laughter Clubs be doing something to see that laughter travels inside the members also? When I requested her to clarify what exactly she meant by laughter travelling inside, she fumbled a little as it was evident that she had not prepared herself for such question. But, making some effort she said that what she really meant was that to be Laughter Club members in the true sense, they should develop the spirit of laughter also. I thanked her for the suggestion and assured her that it would be considered seriously. To be honest, I did this first to be polite, but her suggestion did not leave me, because while I had got used to calls imparting critical comments, this was the first time some one had, I felt, made a constructive suggestion.

On further reflection, the lady's suggestion struck me as very profound. After all, was it not true that laughter would not add up to something very much, if a person did not shed at least some of his negatively, I asked myself.

After some serious discussion amongst those involved in the movement, it was decided that aims of Laughter Clubs be revised from "laugh and be healthy" to "health and happiness through laughter and the spirit of laughter", the spirit of laughter being making not only one's own self happy but also making others happy. Some members interpret this as laughter and the spirit of the laughter becoming a part of the life and living of members.

The above I consider to be an important step along the route of the Laughter Club movement as it brought about a qualitative extension to the focus of the efforts and the action at Laughter Clubs. We now tried to identify actions as steps which would make not only the members happy but would also motivate and equip them to make others happy.

Looking back, I thought it would be a good idea to do something about those members who come for a daily guffaw and had not changed. I thought this was a wonderful platform where people meet every day and it would be a good idea to adopt some resolutions, to bring about changes in their thinking. The idea was to change negative thinking into positive. We started looking for negative emotions and habits which stop us from laughing.

PAYING COMPLIMENTS

One common bad habit most people have is criticizing others just to kill time or just for the heck of it. During morning walks, the common topics of discussion are politics, the price rise, government corruption, pollution, traffic jams, the bad economy etc. followed by problems relating to youngsters and other family members. I could not stop every one of them. But, I thought of replacing negative thoughts with positive ones. To do away with the habit of criticising others, why not start complimenting others and raise their spirits and self esteem? One fine day, I made an announcement after a laughter session was over. "Ladies and gentlemen, today is Monday, and every Monday we are going to resolve that during the week we will pay compliments to others. We will appreciate their good qualities and make more and more friends in our buildings, offices, social circles, etc."

Paying compliments was the first commandment we introduced in our search for identifying various ways and means of sensible living. On Sundays, after the laughter session, we shared our experiences about paying compliments. To whom had club members paid compliments and what were the results? Intially, the response was not very enthusiastic, but some people thought it was a good idea. Many people found it difficult to pay compliments just like that, as it seemed like flattery and sycophancy. I repeatedly made announcements that one of the objectives of Laughter Clubs is health and happiness through laughter. The happiness aimed at is, not only to make one's own self happy but also to make others happy which further results in one's own happiness. One of the ways to make others happy is by paying genuine and deserved compliments to others.

Some members got very good results and they started appreciating their spouses and children in the house, while others said good words to their servants. In India very few people appreciate their wives with words, they may feel affection in their hearts but they may not verbalise their feelings. For example very few people actually say to their wives, "I love you". One fine day one of the members went home after the laughter session and told his wife "You are looking very beautiful', as she was getting up from bed. She wondered what

Laughter session at Ghatkopar (E), Mumbai

has happened to her husband, because he had never said this in their last 25 years of married life. In the first place he had never told his wife before that she was beautiful, but when he said it, the timing was wrong. Had he said these words when she was dressed in her best before going to a party, it would have made more sense.

A social worker from a Laughter Club said thank you to the bus driver while alighing. Everybody was looking at him, as not many people say thank you to bus drivers, taxi drivers or servants in the house. Inspite of initial ridicule and resistance, people have started imbibing the idea because of repeated announcements and reminders. And there is always resistance to any change even if it is for the better. I was surprised to know that many people find it very difficult to compliment others. The human tendency, by and large, is to see only the wrong and bad in others, ignoring the good and then to criticize and condemn. As a result of this tendency, a lot of negative energy is generated and there is unpleasantness, bitterness, intemperance, tension and bad relations all round. Therefore, the idea of sharing their experiences with compliment--paying was to give members an insight on how to gracefully give compliments. How many things can you compliment and in what ways? The most important thing we tell our members, is to look for good qualities in others and then appreciate them. Giving irrelevant, undeserving, unnecessary compliments might look like a gimmick or purse sychopancy.

Is Paying Compliments Necessary?

People of all ages and backgrounds and at all stages of success and failure need love and recognition in order to live happily. Everyone, if he is to function at his best, needs to be noticed and appreciated. Most of us want to be told how we are doing. If our best efforts are met with silence, we tend to become careless, negligent and hostile.

Each one of us has a mental picture of ourselves, a self image. To find life reasonably satisfying, the self image must be one that we can live with and can like. When we are proud of our self image, we feel confident and free to be ourselves. We function at our best. When we are ashamed of our self image, we attempt to hide rather than express ourselves. In such a situation one becomes hostile and hard to get along with. A sort of miracle happens to the person whose self-esteem has been raised. He suddenly starts liking other people better. He becomes kinder and more co-operative with people around him. Praise is a like a polish the helps to keep one's self image bright and sparkling. By raising someone's spirits and adding to someone's self-esteem you make him want to like you and to co-operate with you. To flatter or put into words emotions we don't feel amounts to insincerity which is easily spotted and benefits none.

Withholding a compliment is cheating. It should be passed on as quickly as possible. It might give some unhappy person a moment of joy or help him cope with deep despair. It will help someone defeat the two arch enemies of human happiness - loneliness and insignificance.

Happiness Comes Back

As an artist finds joy in giving beauty to others, so also, anyone who masters the art of praising will find that it blesses the giver as much as the receiver. There is a truth in the saying that "Flowers leave part of their fragrance in the hands that bestow them". If you increase your sense of gratitude and your willingness to express it, you will make the people around happier and you will become a happier person yourself.

How to Pay Compliments

One can pass on compliments in a casual conversation, or by a letter, or a written note. There is yet an other way - that of third party compliments . When someone says something pleasant to you directly, there is possibility of that being discounted as mere politeness or even flattery. There are many others who find it difficult to pay compliments directly as it may cause some embarrassment. They can take recourse to what may be called 'Third party compliments'. This form of appreciation is much easier and could even be more effective. When indirect compliments reach the concerned party they may be better than direct ones, because most people believe that if someone praises you behind your back, he probably means exactly what he says.

When to Pay Compliments

The golden rule of appreciation is - Do it now! Do it while your sense of gratitude is fresh and strong. If you feel a flash of thankfulness, act on it before the impulse goes away.

A Few Examples From Laughter Clubs

Though the idea has not taken off fully, it has already made a good beginning. I would like to cite a few stories.

1. There is a small cobbler who sits at the corner of my lane where I live in Mumbai. I found him fully involved and happy doing shoe

repairing jobs. One fine day I stopped for a while and wanted to express my feelings about him. I said, "My dear sir, you are doing yeoman service to humanity. Do you know that the job you are doing for a few paise, is considered a dirty job by many people?" He smiled and was thrilled to receive such a compliment. After that he smiles at me whenever I pass his shop. I could clearly see his spirits raised by acknowledging his contribution to society.

2. One Mr. Samtani from the Jogger's Park Bandra Laughter Club in Mumbai, wanted to hire a taxi from Bandra to Mahim. Most cabbies refused to take him as the distance was very short and non-lucrative. Suddenly Mr. Samtani remembered compliment magic. He signaled one taxi man and said "Good morning, How are you?" The cabbie was surprised and wondered how come the term *Bada Saab* (big boss) for a small person like a taxi man? He was over-joyed at the gesture and happily took Mr. Samtani to Mahim. Throughout the journey he was talking to his customer and shared his thoughts about various aspects of life these days.

3. On Sundays, during our extra meeting to share the secret, one member said "I didn't pay compliments to anyone but once I was beginning to criticize someone and suddenly my inner voice stopped me saying, "Hey! Hey!! What are you doing? You are a Laughter Club member and you are supposed to compliment others!" That was an achievement I believe.

To conclude, what the Laughter Clubs really seeks to achieve is not only laughter outside us but also laughter within us. Paying compliments would result in what we would like to call "Inner laughter", that is "the spirit of laughter". I often ask Laughter Club members during our monthly meeting, "Why does one go on to make a lot of money, beyond what's needed for one's basic necessities?" It is to get appreciated and noticed. Building a palatial house has no meaning if you don't hold parties and have more and more people appreciate your achievements and taste.

If you spend huge amounts of money only to get appreciation and recognition, there is no need to break your heart in earning that much money. If people spend so much of money in search of compliments, why not give them free and liberally?

On behalf of the Laughter Club International we are building a network of like-minded people who will share their experiences about complimenting others and we plan to publish a book on "How to Compliment Others in How Many Ways?" This would provide a wealth of knowledge from which millions of people will draw inspiration in order to spread happiness. The idea of paying compliments is nothing new. But through the platform of Laughter Clubs it will get manifested rather than remain mere knowledge. By paying compliments, we the members of Laughter Clubs, are developing a conscious habit of praising others and winning hearts. Indirectly, it will help to shun the habit of criticizing others which creates a hostile atmosphere and stops us from laughing.

CHAPTER - 15

Sensible Living: What has Forgiveness to do with Laughter Clubs?

L aughter in Laughter Clubs is not meant to be only outer laughter or physical exercise, but also inner laughter, that is, developing the spirit of laughter by being happy and making others happy. It is a joint effort to search for different formulas for stress-free living. To live in peace and hormony we need to identify and be aware all the time of what stops us from laughing. Going through the various aspects of human behaviour, it was found that there is an entity called the Ego which gets hurt over and again and makes our life miserable, inspite of our best achievements. Among the strange behaviour of human beings, something which has puzzled me though the years is that it takes years to build a relationship and it needs just a stroke to finish off age old ties. Friends and relatives become foes and set out to finish each other, the very same people who earlier could not live without each other. What makes all that difference and causes a change of heart? I was told by my learned friends, it is ego.

We all go through life in a world where even well-meaning people hurt one another. A friend insults or betrays, a parent abuses, a lover ditches and so on. That gives rise to stream of painful memories. If these grudges and grievances are not forgiven, the rancours and resentments keep the old wounds alive. They continue to haunt and harm both the parties physically as well as psychologically. As preached extensively in Jainism, Christianity and many other religions, forgiveness breaks the grip of pain on our minds and opens the doors to the possibility of repairing resentments and grievances, whereas, hate and revenge are totally counterproductive, and in the long run, apologising/forgiving is the best alternative for both the forgiver and the forgiven.

But, it is all easier said than done Still, there is something deep inside us which stops us from asking for forgiveness even if we want to. It sounds humiliating for most people to give an apology. And many people find it difficult to forgive others who have caused a grievous hurt. Even if the hurt is well recognised by both parties, then the question arises, who will ask for forgiveness first?

FACTORS WHICH HINDER APOLOGY/FORGIVENESS

There are certain misconceptions, which hinder recourse to the best alternative of apology/forgiveness. Let us review these misconceptions more realistically, as this will help overcome hurdles.

a) The first misconception is that apologising will depict the apologiser as a weak person and may invite humiliation. This is incorrect and contrary to experience. It is the impression of one who has not tried it earlier. The fact is, however, that apologising requires a lot of moral courage and instead of humiliating, it raises the apologiser in the eyes of the other, which prompts the latter to consider forgiving.

b) Then, again the apologiser feels doubtful about whether the forgiver will accept his apology. Actually most people are understanding and when one admits that he is at fault, it touches the generosity instinct which every person has. Even if your apology is rejected once, it may be due to the deep hurt or sensitivity of a person. If persistent efforts are applied most people will not resist and you will definitely get a chance of peaceful co-existence. If your apology is not accepted, perhaps your expression was not repentant enough to assuage the hurt of the other person.

c) The natural response to deep and unfair hurt is hate, which comes more easily and gives rise to the desire for getting even and hurting back. Therefore, on the face of it, forgiving requires the forgiver to be contrary to his interests and appeals to him to be unnatural and unjust, as his sense of fairness tells him that people must pay for their wrong-doings. For these reasons, the forgiver thinks that forgiving is weakness. These feelings and emotions may be correct on the surface but when examined in depth, it becomes clear that to forgive is to be tough and not weak. It needs lot of guts to let alone a person who has done harm to you. Though the idea of forgiving may appear to be passive to some, genuine forgiveness is a positive act that requires enormous spiritual strength. Therefore, people who ask for an apology and those who consider forgiveness are not ordinary people. It needs a very stable mind to understand in depth the future implications of hate and revenge. In contrast, if the apology is asked for or forgiveness is considered out of fear that the other person may be stronger, the results may not be fruitful in the long run.

d) Another problem which hinders forgiveness is that one person may keep on hurting the other and ask for forgiveness over and again. If it is happening so, the forgiver may choose his stand and communicate it to the apologiser emphatically. But one must not think about this possibility in the very first case.

e) Forgiveness becomes very easy if you analyse the situation and find out if the act of wrongdoing is deliberate or unintended. Calm consideration of the matter will make the hurt person see the truth and then seriously consider the best alternative of forgiveness. Even if the hurt is deliberate, a proper communication of your desire to live in peace will make the other person realise his mistake.

It is very rare the that wrong doer is hundred percent at fault and the person hurt is a hundred per cent innocent. If someone has insulted or hurt you, look deep into yourself if your actions in a small way are responsible for the act. If you can see your contributions, may be in a small way, it becomes much easier to forgive. No person is all good or all bad and everyone has some good and some bad in him. But in practice the application or this truth is one sided. If I am the wrong doer, to minimise the wrong done by me, I say "I am not as bad as I am being made out to be. After all there is so much good in me?" This is very conveniently forgotten and over looked when the wrong doer is someone else. His wrongdoings get exaggerated and good points are ignored. If the forgiver reminds himself that the other person also has something good, it becomes much easier to consider apology or forgiveness.

EFFECTIVE APOLOGY

Many times the apologies are not considered for forgiveness because they are not projected properly. Naturally, an apology must be sincere and satisfy the forgiver for better results. Otherwise the entire effort may go to waste. For an apology to be effective, the following points should be kept in mind.

a) The apology should be direct and the apologier should never pretend to be doing something else.

b) The forgiver has to be made to realise that the apology is really meant. Therefore, the apologiser must not be looking at the ground or elsewhere, but into the eyes of the forgiver, though it may be a bit embarrassing for a moment.

c) The apologier must show readiness to accept responsibility. It should be a total acceptance. One should avoid making excuses because that dilutes the apology. A no excuses apology leaves both the parties feeling better about themselves.

d) Most of the time, it may not be enough to merely say "I am sorry" because the victim wants to see that the apologiser is really feeling bad and looks upset. If the apologiser can put a bit more expression into his apology it is more likely to calm down the recipient.

Effective Forgiveness

Like in effective apology, ineffective forgiveness can also render all efforts fruitless. For forgiveness to be effective:

a) It must be gracious.

b) It must be sincere and show a change of heart on the part of the forgiver.

c) It must not appear as if being done as a favour to the appologiser. It must not be accompanied by warnings or threats. Rather, it should suggest that the apologiser avoids such provocations in future so that both can live in peace and harmony.

d) Acceptance of an apology is very important. Therefore, the forgiver must be seen to be really accepting it. Since most people find it difficult to apologise, the acceptance could be by words like "I know it must have been hard for you to apologise and I very much appreciate your saying that." It could be by inviting the other party for a cup of tea. Another effective acceptance is by writing a letter with will have better registration. Such symbolic gestures can strengthen the bond of forgiveness. Holding of the hand and a couple of hugs, if appropriate, will add flavour to the future relationship.

NEVER RE-OPEN OLD FILES

The two words 'forgive and forget' generally go together. And rightly so, because if the forgiver is not able to forget, he would not have really forgiven. Forgetting takes some time. That, however, is no cause for worry, because if there is genuine forgiving, the wounds will heal and forgetting will eventually, come. Forgetting, however, does not mean obliterating the whole event from memory. What has to be forgotten is the hurt, resentment and bitterness. Details of the happenings, which remain in the memory, without bitterness and hurt, could serve the useful purpose of enabling others to learn from the experience. All the best efforts will be nullified if one tries to open old files at the slightest provocation. I have seen people making each other's lives miserable for years together, refering to an event which has happened twenty years before.

To illustrate this point we narrate and enact a story as to how hunters catch monkeys. They fix a box with iron parts placed at such a distance that a monkey can pass his empty hand to take the bananas kept inside. Once the monkey holds a banana, it becomes difficult for him to pull his hand out of the box. If it has the wisdom of leaving the banana it could go free. By holding on to the banana, he gets caught. In our workshops we actually tell one of the participants to hold a banana and try to take his hand out, which does not happen. Taking a cue from the story, we remind out members, whenever you make the mistake of opening old grievances, remember that you are acting like a monkey holding on to his banana.

ADVANTAGES OF APOLOGY/FORGIVENESS

Experts have come to realise that forgiving and forgetting is one of the first means of defence. These are untapped and least understood sources of healing power.

a) If a person realises his mistake, but does not pick up the courage to apologise, that does not benefit him any way. Rather, he is perpetuating endless self-punishment. Seeking forgiveness can free him of that punishment.

b) In a strained relationship both the parties live under stress. An apology and forgiveness can result in new happiness for both.

c) It breaks pain's grip on our minds and open the doors of new possibilities. A new beginning could arise from past pain.

d) Forgiveness transforms hostility into helpfulness and lifts the spirits of both the forgiver and the forgiven.

e) It is said that the most important ingredient in forgiveness is love, and at its best, forgiveness is done for those person who are our loved ones and have hurt us. The forgiveness, in such cases, is at its most powerful, renewing friendships, marriage and careers.

f) Hate and revenge disturb the harmony of the entire family. Hate, whether passive or active, is a malignancy that grows, eats you from within and keeps on releasing harmful chemicals that give rise to a battery of illnesses. And vegeance never evens the score. That leads to an endless spate of retaliation. History is full of such examples, where a little act of revenge has wiped out entire families and has led to war between nations. Mahatma Gandhi once said that if we all live by an "eye for an eye" kind of justice, the whole of mankind would be blind.

DOUBLE BENEFIT

There are many situations in life where one is provoked into state of anger. If you get angry with someone who is bothering you and fight with him unavoidably, there is a lot to be achieved by saying 'sorry' after sometime when your temple has cooled down. You may fire your child, your family member, an employee or a neighbour. They will have hurt feelings even if they are not able to express then. But if you pick up the courage to go up to the person with whom you fought a short while earlier and say, "Sorry. I got angry with you, but I got upset because I didn't like the way you behaved with me." Here, by saying sorry you are neutralising the hurt feeling inflicted by your outburst and you can take this opportunity to remind the person once again, about the reason why you got angry.

FRIDAY FOR FORGIVENESS

In the Jain religion there is a festival once in a year called *"Michhami Dukkadam"* meaning asking for forgiveness. On one particular day after prayers in the temple, people ask for forgiveness from each other. Also there are forgiveness cards like new year greeting cards, which are sent out to relatives, friends and business colleagues asking for forgiveness, if they have hurt them directly or indirectly. Since ancient days, it has been a good platform for those who feel inhibited to verbalise their apologies directly to the people concerned.

I attended one such function and was highly impressed with the idea, and thought it worthwhile to implement forgiveness through Laughter Clubs. Somewhere in March 1997, I explained this idea to the members and most of them liked it. Doing is once a year might not help to register this idea, and may take too long to experiment with various practical aspects of it. Therefore, I thought, why not remind the members every Friday? There is no relation of a particular day with forgiveness. Every Friday the anchor person makes an announcement, "Dear Friends, today is Friday, our forgiveness day. If you think you have hurt someone and you have not been on talking terms with somebody for a long time, this is the time to muster some courage and offer an apology, saying, "Knowingly or unknowingly if I have hurt you in any way, I am sorry." Invite them for a cup of tea or to come over for dinner, in order to make a new beginning.

LAUGHTER CLUBS AND FORGIVENESS

Designating Friday as "Forgiveness Day" by Laughter Clubs, is not a gimmick or an empty slogan. If properly implemented, it will be a valuable means of enhancing the inner laughter of members. By making repeated announcements and doing a sort of dress rehearsal every Friday, the chances of getting this idea registered are much higher. The trouble with most people is that even if they want to say sorry, it is difficult to verbalise the feelings. By doing it over and again we are making it a conscious habit so that it comes out easily when required. I myself have been benefited immensely from this idea. I must have renewed over as dozen relationships by giving an apology. As a matter of fact, many bonds have become much stronger than before.

WHAT DOES NOT CONSTITUTE FORGIVENESS?

Forgiveness is the ability to control anger by understanding the situation in depth and then choosing the right kind of response instead of a prompt reaction. It prevents generation of anger and enables one to control the emotion of revenge. Forgiveness is kindness, tenderness, affinity and love expressed after careful thought.

Hypocrisy is to forgive outwardly and cultivate revenge, enmity and a desire to punish inwardly. It is not forgiveness. If one forgives under the threat that "My enemy or opponent may harass me if I don't forgive," it is not real forgiveness. If greed and temptation are motives behind forgiving? "If I don't forgive my motive will not be served", then it is not real forgiveness. If your ego is dictating forgiveness. "I am powerful, I am the master and only I can forgive him and save him and in return can get my things done to my convenience", it is not forgiveness. In short, forgiveness originating from ego, fear, hypocrisy, greed, lust etc. is not real forgiveness. Selfless, motiveless, unperverted manifestation of love, kindness and affection is forgiveness.

CHAPTER - 16

Laughter Clubs:
Now Developing into
Close-knit Communities

O ngoing research shows that people suffering from depression are more prone to many illnesses like high blood pressure, heart attacks and cancer. Depression also affects the immune system adversely. Common causes of depression are social isolation and a diminishing family value system. These are much more in western countries but are now slowly affecting the east also. Laughter Clubs have helped many people to get rid of their antidepressant pills in a short period of time. The magic which has worked wonders is the friendship and brotherhood gained from Laughter Clubs. Laughter Clubs are fast developing into close-knit communities.

Laughter is an important tool in our social interaction. It is not only a biological release or a cognitive process, but more importantly it is a social psychological phenomenon, which initiates and facilitates communication. With the spread of Laughter Clubs in every locality, each club has taken the shape of a small community, wherein its members experience a sense of affiliation and belonging to the group. Clubs are turning into large "Laughing Families".

SOCIAL GLUE

The affiliation, in more than one way, has been positive for most of members. These clubs are now not only responsible for enhancement of our physical health, but also for safeguarding our emotional health and, more importantly, communicating harmoniously. Laughter is a common language. It knows no religion and has no gender bias. There is no discrimination according to caste, creed or colour. Laughter is a powerful emotion and a social glue. When Steve Wilson, a psychologist and joyologist from the United States visited some Laughter Clubs in Mumbai, he had the unique experience of participating in a laughter session at Juhu Beach.

In a matter of the few minutes that he spent laughing with so-called strangers, it appeared at the end of the session, as if he knew everyone in that group. There was a strange feeling of closeness with them. Many of our visitors from all over the world share similar views. Thinkers, whether they are sociologists, psychologists, behaviourists or historians for that matter, have always believed that 'Man is a social animal'. We are very well aware of the fact that our behaviour is the result of social values and norms and we all survive on the basis of our social interactions. And there is no doubt that sociability of any kind is considered definitely worth cultivating.

Research conducted in various fields has provided mounting evidence to support the fact that people who belong to a network of community, friends and relatives are happier and healthier, better able to cope with stress and remarkably resistant to emotional and physical ills. Each Laughter Club, with no monetary inclination, has become a close-knit community where people enjoy the caring and warmth of its members. More important, people form close ties with others, irrespective of the economic stratum one belongs to. Prof. Dennis T. Jaffe, Ph. D., a Professor of Psychology at Saybook Institute in San Francisco, has found that, "A close-knit community can act as a protective envelope against stresses of environment." Belonging to the Indian subcontinent we are very fortunate, since our culture supports the family value system. But now a growing western influence has slowly started taking its toll. Today, due to materialization, people have become more self-centered and socially isolated with a rapidly changing social system. Even the way in which we view our elders has changed. A feeling of being worthy and of importance to others is essential not only for a person's self esteem but also for emotional health. When an individual is younger this is a natural experience, because a family is dependent on one another irrespective of whether you are a man or a woman.

Being a man you are more often looked upon for economic security and being a woman, for ensuring a happy, well settled home. Though this pattern is not a given rule, it is not uncommon either. But when there is a transition from youth to old age, this is when perception changes. Evidence from research suggests that in communities where elders are considered a source of wisdom, they are not abandoned, as is the case in other societies. The mortality rates are much lower when compared to other societies. In Laughter Clubs, a majority of members are from an older group, but nowadays many youngsters have also started coming in because of the value addition and health benefits.

ISOLATION IS SICKNESS

In a recent study, participants said they had experienced ties within a Laughter Club such as those in every close-knit family, wherein not only an individual's happiness but also one's sorrows are shared. And hence, it is this sense of social worth that is reinforced by belonging to an accepting and caring community. We ask ourselves the question, What acts as a buffer to stress? The answer is: our spouses, our friends, our siblings, in other words, our social network.

In modern society, where social isolation is becoming a sickness, Laughter Clubs are a welcome introduction to bring back the social value system. I am proud to say that the friendship and brotherhood in Laughter Clubs have made people much more secure than their non-member relatives and friends. I would like to quote an example of a senior member from the Johnson Garden Laughter Club, who fell sick and was admitted to a hospital. He burst into tears of joy when he found his room flooded with flowers from visitors from the Laughter Club, when none of his family members and relatives turned up.

A TOUCHING INCIDENCE

Another incident which I will never forget is when I visited the Laughter Club of Bandra Reclamation in Mumbai, where members laugh everyday in the compound of a temple. At the end of one particular laughter session, the birthday celebrations of a 78-year-old lady were held. This club has a unique way of celebrating birthdays. All the members surrounded the birthday baby and sang a happy birthday song for her and danced around her in a circle. Later, she was taken to the temple a few yards away where she was made to sit on a chair in front of the Ganpati idol. She was offered a coconut, flowers and sweets by the priest and then many Laughter Club members touched her feet. Throughout the celebrations, tears were rolling down her cheeks. They were nothing else but tears of joy. I had read in books about these tears, but was fortunate enough to see them in reality. This is the Laughter Club we are talking about. This is the Laughing Family the whole world is awaiting.

A Laughter Club, in many ways, provides a protective shell that safeguards our emotional well-being. And it is because of this emotional well-being that we can have a physiologically sound system that would determine our resistance to disease. Laughter Clubs have

brought a lot of people together, the consequence being an awareness that one is not alone with one's problems.

HOW LAUGHTER CLUB MEMBERS SOCIALISE

The process of socializing starts from the beginning, the day the
member joins the Laughter Club. Most laughter sessions are held at
public parks, beaches and open grounds where people go for their
morning walks. In our initial survey we found that same people who
are laughing together used to come for a morning walk for years
and never knew each other. They came closer when they started
laughing together. Laughter is a powerful positive emotion and it
changes the electromagnetic fields around your body and builds a
positive aura. Due to laughter in a group, inhibitions are broken
down and a person becomes more receptive. And it is a very happy
socialising that keeps growing as one laughs more and more. It
brings about nearness, companionship and camaraderie, flowering
into a kind of social support.

CELEBRATIONS

Laughter groups have started celebrating different festivals belonging
to all communities in their own styles. This has helped to bring
about communal harmony amongst members. Like this, throughout
the year club members meet at least once in two months. They sing,
they dance and they eat together, without any discrimination between rich and poor.

FUN GAMES

With more than 25,000 members in less than four years, Laughter
Clubs are being recognised as a public movement. Though there is
no membership fee, we are organising seminars, health workshops,
yoga and meditation camps from time to time. Many companies are
coming forward to sponsor these events to get them public milage.
Fun games are regularly organised where members have fun-filled

healthy competition with each other, let themselves go and enjoy the warmth of each other's company.

OUTINGS AND PICNICS

Outings and picnics in a big group have their own fun, especially if participants are all Laughter Club members. Most clubs organise outings, picnics and excursions and feel happy together. They sing, dance and play fun games and have some new idea or another because there is no dearth of new ideas in such a big group. People have admitted that group picnics are much more enjoyable than family picnics. Another added advantage is massive group discounts. They can have much more with the same amount of money.

All tourist places offer heavy discounts to Laughter Club members, sensing a big potential of regular business from them. The extent of socialising through Laughter Clubs can be gauged by the frequency and extent of participation in the outings.

Many groups organise trips for 3-4 days, several times a year. In between there are one- day picnics, at least once in two months. Now the frequency is on the rise as members are exploring new destinations all over the country. The formats of picnics are being shared by different club members to make them more interesting and enjoyable. Through our central body, the Laughter Club International, we are sharing all the good things in life to keep motivation levels high.

HOLIDAY-CUM-LEARNING

In our new model outings, we are trying to make our holidays more value-based by adding some health-building activities like learning yoga, meditation, acupressure and different non-drug, alternative healing systems. It is 75% fun and 25% learning. With our ever expanding network we are introducing new projects to add more colour to Laughter Clubs.

CELEBRATING BIRTHDAYS

Many members are senior citizens and they have long since abandoned the idea of celebrating birthdays. Now they have suddenly come alive. There are many members who have celebrated their birthdays for the first time in their lives. Why not be proud of our existence? In Laughter Clubs, birthdays are celebrated in a very simple and affectionate manner. Some do it with the usual song sung in chorus and by presenting flowers, others give out special greeting cards made on a computer. In some cases, talented members compose a special poem for the occasion. There is yet another way: to make the member wear a funny cap and give him a whistle to blow. This is just a beginning, wait and watch for more ideas. You will be surprised how celebrative Laughter Club members can become.

PROJECT "CHALO CINEMA" (GO FOR MOVIES)

On April 1, 1999, we celebrated All Fools Day - the idea was to make fun of yourself and try to laugh at yourself. It was a hilarious function, the details of which are given in another chapter. On that day we launched yet another social project "Chalo Cinema". The theme of this project is to go out for a movie in a group. With the advent of television and cable networks, people have forgotten to visit theatres which used to provide much needed outings for many. People have become too lazy to go for a movie alone or with the family as different members have their own engagements.

This idea was experimented with by a group of people from Muktanand Laughter Club in Mumbai. After seeing its success, we suggested that all the clubs organise block bookings for a cinema show. One of the group members would go and see the movie before it is offered to a group to cover the possibility of wrong selection. This project took off very well as many groups implemented this programme in the first month itself. It was suggested that they not only watch movies but also go for dramas, dance shows, musical nites, comedy shows and to the circus. To date, more and more news has been pouring in about the success of the programme. People enjoyed the companiable experience. Some of them went to see a movie after a span of 10-15 years. They were thrilled and decided to go more frequently and in larger numbers.

INTER CLUB EXCHANGE PROGRAMMES

Socialisation is not restricted among the members of a particular Laughter Club but goes beyond that. While celebrating anniversaries, invitations are extended to other clubs in town. Representative of different groups are called and honoured during the function. Not only that, some groups even go for picnics together. This is further strengthening the relationship between the members of various clubs.

Extending this idea further, we have started inter-club exchange programmes under which a group of Laughter Club members (generally 10-20) would visit other cities and the host club would arrange to provide them with a home-stay on a voluntary basis. The visiting team will have to pay for their travel arrangements. The boarding, lodging and sight-seeing would be looked after by the host club. This will provide Laughter Club members from all over the country with the opportunity to visit different places and while staying with families, they would understand different cultures. This arrangement is entirely on a mutual basis. The visiting members who enjoy a family stay must reciprocate by hosting people from other cities.

Slowly, when we set up Laughter Clubs all over the world, it will provide an opportunity for the world community to come together and visit different countries in a most economical and interesting way. This project is still in its experimental stages. Some groups have already visited each other with encouraging results. In India I see very bright prospects as Indians are very hospitable people. I am sure we will be successful on an international platform too.

CHAPTER - 17

Laughter Therapy in the Workplace

The growing popularity of Laughter Clubs all over India, and the interest shown by many who have visited these clubs from all over the world have made one point very clear - these clubs are no laughing matter. While tens of thousands are taking to this unique therapy, there are many who wished to join a Laughter Club, but could not do so because of time constraints. Most clubs start quite early, between 6.30 a.m. and 7 a.m. and they are held at public parks where people go for a morning walk. This is the time many office goers cannot come, because they have to leave early for office. Quite a few women cannot participate because they have to send their children to school and their husbands to office. While there are others who sleep late and find it difficult to get up early, but all the same would like to join the laughter session if the time was suitable. Most members are regular walkers who combine their morning walks with laughter.

In India, climatic conditions are favourable for regular walks throughout the year, but I was told by my friends that this would not be possible in many western countries when the mercury dips significantly and it is freezing cold for months together. Also, there is some difficulty in the rainy season when very few people come out for their walks. The only alternative, I thought, was to hold laughter sessions in their work places. I was excited about this idea because the majority of Laughter Club members were from the upper and upper middle classes. Moreover, they were fifty plus, senior citizens and the very young. Lower, middle and working class people were not able to participate in laughter sessions because they had to leave early for work.

FEAR OF INDISCIPLINE

Initially, many people showed interest, but such proposals did not materialise because of some hesitation about any thing new being started and that too a funny concept. Maybe they feared that this might be ridiculed, or it may cause indiscipline. I wrote to many companies, corporate houses, medium and small sized factories. Many bosses thought the workers might not understand the concept well. Many of them, and rightly so, were waiting for its bonafides to be proved. I went on to give seminars and demonstrations in many offices and factories. I found some resistance from the management, who were not very keen on mixing with their workers, because they feared that the workers might not respect them or might disobey them if they laughed together. Usually, they would send their managers to attend the sessions and they themselves refused to come out of their cabins.

My happiness knew no bounds when I heard the news that Mr. H. S. Kaka, the owner of a small factory, has already started laughter sessions on a daily basis with his 10-15 workers in one of the suburbs of Mumbai. Mr. Kaka himself was a member of one of the Laughter Clubs. Quickly I traced him and went to see the factory. I found most of the workers between the ages of 25-40 years and happily doing the therapy. Though their technique was not up to the mark, they were quite happy with their morning guffaws. Then came an invitation from a Managing Director and Chairman of a Pharmaceutical company (Litaka Pharma Ltd.) in Pune near Mumbai.

DYNAMIC YOUNG MAN

On 2nd May, 1998, for the first time Laughter Therapy was introduced in a corporate house. Initially 150 employees of the company including the Chairman, Executives and Security Guards learnt the various techniques of yogic laughter. It is being done during all three shifts and the employers are finding it very useful. Insipired by the positive results, Mr. Anil Bora the Managing Director has planned to introduced this therapy in another factory which he owns.

There is one small factory in Mumbai, Electrical Products of India (EPI), which produced amazing results with Laughter Therapy. The young and dynamic Managing Director, Mr. Pinak Marfatia, just 27 years old, leads a group of 25 workers in laughter every morning before starting work. The well organised laughter session is followed by birthday celebrations of members and in between during the day, they all dance together to recharge their spirits.

The beauty of this organisation is that the boss himself comes down to the shopfloor and conducts the laughter sessions and dances with his workers. According to Mr. Marfatia, there is significant improvement in interpersonal relationships.

Employees are working more and they are carrying the laughing spirit to their houses also. "They suffer from fewer coughs, colds and headaches than before. The productivity too has increased," he said. Many people from all over the world have visited the factory and this success was reported in many papers, magazines and television channels.

PRODUCTIVITY THROUGH LAUGHTER

Today business houses and industries all over the world are facing the worst ever recession. Profits are declining and workers are hard pressed to match their incomes with rising prices. Executives are pressed hard to step up sales in the face of fierce competition.

The members of the business community (Managers, Sales and Marketing Personnel, Executives, Administrators) are living very stressful lives. Most diseases like high blood pressure, heart disease, peptic ulcers, insomnia, depression, allergies and even cancer have some relation to stress. This contributes to absenteeism, poor performance and addictions.

In Japan, it is a regular practice to do some physical exercises in the office premises in the morning, before employees start their work. All the members of the company, from Managing Director to peons, participate. We believe that introducing Laughter Therapy in corporate houses is a very significant and worthwhile idea. It can help to improve inter-personal relationships at all levels in an organization, replacing mutual lack of trust and confidence with a more positive outlook and co-operative attitude towards one's colleagues and subordinates. This should, in turn, definitely help to improve the prevalent work environment and overall performance of an organization.

ADVANTAGES OF LAUGHTER THERAPY IN CORPORATE HOUSES

❖ Laughter Therapy increases oxygen levels in the body and releases endorphins (feel-good hormones) from the brain cells. Daily laughter exercise will bring a sense of well-being and feeling of freshness throughout the day. Participants learn to wear smiles on their faces.

❖ It will help reduce inhibitions, increase self-confidence and develop leadership qualities among participants. Starting the day on a positive note will improve interpersonal relationships and hence performance. Bosses and subordinates will work with a better frame of mind, rather than fearing each other.

❖ Deep breathing, neck and shoulder stretching exercises will help remove stiffness and pain resulting from stress and a sedentary lifestyle.

❖ Laughter Therapy increases body resistance by stimulating the immune system of the body. Regular laughing sessions will significantly reduce the frequency of coughs, colds and throat and chest infections.

❖ It will help to control many diseases like high blood pressure, heart disease, irritability, insomnia, anxiety, depression, allergic disorders, asthma, bronchitis, tension and migraine headaches, as well as aches and pains due to arthritis, cervical spondylitis and backache.

❖ Laughter Therapy is one of the easiest types of meditation which brings you instant relaxation. It disconnects your mind from the physical world. While laughing you cannot think of anything else. In other types of meditation you need to concentrate a lot to take your mind away from unwanted thoughts, which is easier said than done.

❖ As a group effort, all the Laughter Club members try to identify and remove the negative factors like guilt, anger, fear, jealousy and ego, which stop us from laughing. They cultivate the spirit of laughter by following ways and means of sensible living, like paying compliments, the art of forgiveness and understanding human relationships.

❖ By holding periodic seminars we impart practical training to help members to discover their own sense of humour and celebrate life, in spite of its tough challenges.

❖ Through practise of Yogic Laughter we want to make people understand that happiness and laughter are states of mind and should be unconditional, irrespective of the ups and downs of life. If you are in a happy and positive frame of mind you can solve your problems in a much better way.

❖ To make people believe in the philosophy that motion creates emotion. If you act like a happy man first thing in the morning your chemistry will become real.

❖ To make people aware of the power of group effort. Anything practiced in a group becomes easier to manifest rather than trying to do the same thing alone. Not only do we laugh and do stretching exercise together, we are also learning to understand the ways and means of sensible living all together.

❖ Every human being has infinite potential to perform and achieve anything he desires, but most of his power lies dormant and untapped. Through Laughter Therapy and meditation, one can release one's infinite potential and achieve greater heights in life.

At present there are four small factories in Mumbai and one pharmaceutical company in Pune who are very happily practising laughter therapy.

Laughter at Work place : We are happiest people in the world......Laughter keeps you fresh throughout the day.

"Very pleased to meet you"; Factory manager greeting the workers with a laughter. "Please don't mind if at all I shout at you during the day".

Dr. Madan Kataria training 25 factory workers of a small factory at Mumbai. They all laugh first thing in the morning before starting the work.

Mr. Pinak Marfatia, the Chairman and Managing Director of Engineering Productors of India (EPI) is very happy even during recession in the industry.

"No problem! The productivity has gone up ever since we started laughing", says Pinak Marfatia of EPI.

Less absenteeism, coughs and colds, the workers remain cheerful
and carry the spirit to their homes.

"Laughter is the cheapest, less time consuming and results are amazing"
says young entrepreneur Mr. Marfatia strongly recommended.

CHAPTER - 18

Laughter Sessions Among School Children

O ne thing which always embarrassed me was someone ask ing me, "What age group of people come for laughing sessions? The answer was those who are 40 plus, senior citizens and retired people. Does that give the impression that Laughter Clubs are only meant for elderly people who have nothing else to do? Why didn't youngsters come for laughter sessions?"

Though school children used to enjoy laughter sessions during their vacations, they were not able to come regularly because most laughter sessions start quite early between 6.30 - 7a.m. This is the time children have to hurry up to catch their buses. College classes too start quite early and most youngsters are not aware of the benefits of laughter therapy. They think it is more for those who are suffering from some kind of ailment. Moreover they are interested in heavy workouts like jogging, swimming, gymnastics, cycling and aero-

bics. Nowadays many middle-aged women have started coming as they found laughter to be very beneficial.

Among the participants in many clubs there were school teachers and they kept experimenting with small groups of children in their schools, but nobody came up with a solid proposal. The apprehension about implementing laughter exercise could be the fear of the nuisance children might create during their classes. But if it is projected as a authentic yogic exercise and done in a properly structured manner to be executed by popular teachers, it will definitely bring good results.

THE FIRST PROPOSAL

One fine day I received a telegram from Mr. Madhukar Parashar, Principal of Progressive English High School, Aurangabad, in Maharashtra State, inviting me to start yogic laughter for school children. "I want to see my children smiling when they enter their classes," said Mr. Parashar. He had read about the Laughter Clubs of Mumbai in several newspapers. The principal was so keen about laughter that he introduced a few jokes in the morning after prayers, to make his pupils laugh. He kept on calling me over the telephone and sent me a couple of telegrams requesting me to visit his school at the earliest.

I distinctly remember the date. It was 21st October 1996, the day I was waiting for my first session with 300 boys and girls between the ages of 4 and 15, along with 50 odd parents and 25 school teachers. Everybody was waiting in suspense to see what was going to happen in the next hour. I always loved making children laugh, because it is easy to make them giggle and chuckle. During the demonstration they were bursting with laughter and sometimes it was very difficult to stop them. I wanted them to be quiet before we could demonstrate the next type of laughter. I requested the principal and senior teachers to keep them quiet. In my four years of experience, I have observed that when I am with adults, I tell them, "Come on, Laugh! Laugh!!" and they find it difficult to laugh. But whenever I went to any school for a laughter session, I found it difficult to stop the children laughing. They would laugh at any silly thing.

One very striking feature was that younger children, below the age of six, were less inhibited and were laughing more vibrantly than their senior schoolmates. Teachers were also enjoying the session but they too were a bit inhibited. The head teacher and P.T. teacher took the intiative to learn the various techniques so as to continue laughter sessions everyday for 5 to 10 minutes after the school prayers in the morning. The children were overjoyed and showed their willingness to laugh everyday.

The very next day we left Aurangabad and we were kept updated with encouraging reports of laughter sessions in the school. Many children wrote me letters requesting me to come again. This was the only school which practiced laughter everyday. But my joy didn't last long enough. After one year when I visited Aurangabad for a stress management workshop in an industrial house, I discovered that the Principal, Mr. Parashar had had a heart attack a few months back and due to his demise the laughter sessions were stopped. After that, the Caretakar of the school didn't take any intiative to start it again.

Following that I must have given demonstrations in more than 25 schools in various cities. The concept was appreciated but so far none has implemented it. May be they are waiting for its bonafides to be proved. May be they are afraid of the nuisance the children might create as they chant Ho Ho Ha Ha. Meanwhile, many teachers are trying out laughter sessions in the classes in a small way and finding it very useful in creating a positive mood.

WHY CHILDREN OF TODAY NEED TO LAUGH MORE

a) While children are said to be the ideal models of mirth, too much stress of modern studies has taken a toll of their laughter it seems. They are loaded with too much information. The subjects which we were taught in the tenth standard, poor kids are now forced to study in 5th standard. Competition is very tough these days, and to stay in the race they have to cut down on their play time and attend extra tutions. Thus, their stress levels are mounting. More and more children are committing suicide because they can't stand the fierce competition. Laughter sessions everyday will help to reduce these stress levels.

b) Today's children abandon the spirit of fun, play and laughter at an early age. This was very obvious when we had combined sessions with children from 1st to 10th standards. While children below 3rd and 4th standards were having a great time, the seniors were a bit more reserved. Daily laughter will help them retain their spirit of laughter and playfulness.

c) Children of today will have to face tough challenges to survive in this competitive world. If they can be taught to handle their emo-

156

tions effectively, and learn the ways and means of sensible living through laughter therapy, they can live much happier lives.

BENEFITS OF LAUGHTER THERAPY TO CHILDREN

1. Regular laughter sessions will increase oxygen supply to improve their mental functions and academic performance.

2. It will reduce stress during examination time. As a matter of fact before entering the exam hall, they should be made to laugh for 10 minutes to reduce anxiety.

3. Laughter Therapy will increase stamina and breathing capacity to help them excel in sports activity. It will be very relaxing before competitive sports events.

4. It will increase the level of relaxation and reduce nervousness and stage fright. It will also help children to be more extrovert and develop self confidence.

5. They will suffer fewer attacks of coughs, colds, throat and chest infections, as laughter helps to build good immunity against common infections.

6. If yogic deep breathing is practised in between two types of laughter, it will help them develop mental stability. If cheerfulness becomes a way of life, they will have a positive attitude even during hard times. Laughter will also help them enhance their creative abilities.

CHAPTER - 19

Laughing Session with The Blind: a Wonderful Experience

T here was a time in the initial two years when every week some news or the other about Laughter Clubs used to ap pear in various newspapers and magazines. For media people the idea of Laughter Clubs was fascinating. In October 1997, I remember receiving a phone call from Mr. Dinesh Saryia, requesting me to come to an institute for the blind in Dadar, Mumbai, and demonstrate the laughter techniques for 60-80 young girls, mostly below 12 years. Mr. Saryia told me, "We have heard a lot about your Laughter Clubs, why not make blind people laugh?"

Dinesh must have been around 25 and his vision was diminishing due to retinitis pigmentosa, a disease which gradually leads to blindness. He expressed his desire to meet me in my office and work out the details. I said yes, a bit hesitantly, because I was wondering how I would make blind people laugh.

Normally, we laugh in a group and stimulate each other by looking in each other's eyes. This is how we are able to convert forced laughter into genuine chuckles. After two days young Dinesh came to my office with a colleague who was blind too. They spent nearly half-an-hour with me and one thing which was very peculiar was that while talking they were smiling all the time, which is very rare in normal individuals. Suddenly I recalled my visits to blind homes during my college days when I observed that most blind people have inbuilt smiles on their faces when they talk, for what reason, I don't know. I was also aware of the fact the blind people become extraordinarily talented in music, weaving skills and other arts. Both the youngsters were very happy and enthusiastic about our visit to the blind home. I went along with four Laughologists by local train and it took us half-an-hour to find the institute building in that congested locality.

We were given a warm welcome at the Institute's Annual Readers Day function, where we found many normal young volunteers who were committed to helping the blind students. Throughout the year whenever they got spare time they used to come and read to blind students. After the initial ceremony, we asked a group of 30-40 blind girls to come out in the open and experience the joy of laughing exercise. Initially the little girls were hesitant and giggling among themselves, saying, "How can we laugh like that?" At the same time they were amused with the idea of laughing in a group for no reason. After ten minutes of persuasion they joined the group of adults outside in the compound. I was still not sure, whether I would be able to make them laugh.

THE SOUND OF LAUGHTER IS ALSO CONTAGIOUS

One needs to look at other people to intiate laughter. Eye contact is an important factor in eliciting genuine giggles. But I was proved wrong when I experimented with that particular laughter session. For the first time I realised that the sound of laughter is also infectious. As the session progressed the quality of laughter improved. The small little girls were laughing non-stop and it was indeed difficult to stop them. They were laughing heartily as if they were starved of this natural gift. So much so, two girls had tears rolling down their cheeks. To my surprise, hesitant looking youngsters were laughing more vibrantly than adults and mature people who joined the session too. At the end, quiet looking girls suddenly became talkative and asked me, "Uncle, when will you come again to make us laugh?" I did say I would come back soon, but there was no further response from the organisers. I requested the principal and authorities of the blind institute to carry out laughter sessions every day. I was willing to send a few senior members of Laughter Clubs to train the anchors. But it was not to be. I never got any call from there. To me it seems, those little girls are still waiting for me and one day I will go there, even if uninvited.

This was a unique experience to remember and I would like to bring smiles and laughter to the faces of millions of blind people all over the world. It may bring a fresh ray of hope to their sight-deprived lives. I am determined to form a task force of senior people from Laughter Clubs who want to do some social work and who have plenty of time. I need some funds to implement this scheme. I call upon social workers and philanthropists to join hands with me in this mission.

CHAPTER - 20

"Woman Power" in Laughter Clubs

I have always held women in high esteem as far as health is concerned. Man is supposed to be stronger then woman in many ways, but when it comes to health and stress management, women are far ahead of their counterparts. Women have always been more concerned about the health of their families and they are always in the forefront whenever any health-building activity is being considered. One of the unique features of Laughter Clubs is the enthusiastic participation from the fairer sex. In a conservative country like India, it requires a lot of courage for a woman to come out in a public place and laugh aloud for no reason.

In the beginning when we started the first Laughter Club in Mumbai, we had only two women, as most other were not sure of what exactly would happen and how useful these funny proceedings would be. Initially many women used to watch from a distance and get amused, but they didn't have the courage to join the group as they were waiting for more women to join. Slowly, over a period of time, when we learnt to laugh without jokes and the word started spreading about the breathing and stretching exercises based on yoga, more and more women started participating. Most participants are aged 40-50 plus, as younger women have to send their children to school and their husbands to office. But during vacations they used to come along with their children and enjoyed the fun. Many regretted their non-availability in the mornings.

After working hard in their kitchens and at the chores of running a household, our Laughter Clubs provided a new platform for them to give vent to their bottled-up emotions. I must admit that the presence of more and more women provided authenticity to our movement. People in India believe that if women are there in Laughter Clubs there must be something good about them, otherwise they would not endorse them so enthusiastically.

MORE DEVOTED

In my experience, when it comes to laughing with no reason, it was much easier to make women laugh than men. The absurdity and stupidity factor works better with women. Even the infectiousness of laughter is much better in them. I do not understand the reason for this. Maybe they are less logic-oriented than men. They operate more out of devotion. That is the reason why more women are to be found at spiritual discourses and religious activities.

MORE FUN LOVING

It may be due to their long association with children while bringing them up, that women are more fun-loving. All the fun activities during various functions conducted by Laughter Clubs are efficiently executed by women. While playing fun games they are more absorbed and they don't look as if they are doing them just to kill time.

162

Recently we launched a new project 'Chalo cinema' (Go for movies), because going to a theatre in a group has its own charm. We advised all club members to go for a movie, drama or to the circus at least once in two months. The project took off very well and again the women were more enthusiastic.

ONLY WOMEN CLUB

There were 30-40 per cent of women in all the Laughter Clubs for a year or so. After that there were some drop-outs among men because of their other commitments, but the attendance of women started growing. In many clubs, women outnumber men. They seem more committed and their drop-out rate is much lower. At many places there are 100% women only clubs!

My joy knew no bounds when I was informed that there was a 'women only club' going very strong in one of the suburbs in Mumbai, where they laugh at 6 p.m. every evening for half-an-hour. Surprisingly, there were 60-70 women gathered in the compound of a building and laughing out loud. Normally, we don't suggest that people start a Laughter Club in a building compound because even if one person complains about noise pollution, the club will land up with problems.

I was told by the confident group leader that there is no chance of any complaint, because members from each and every house come down to participate in the laughter sessions. Seeing is believing. I went there and found amazing enthusiasm. A majority of members were working women. They come back home at 5.30 p.m. and start their guffaws at 6 p.m. I never expected this to happen but I was truly happy to see this development.

LAUGH LIKE
A RED INDIAN

CHAPTER - 21

How Can You Start a Laughter Club in Your Area?

WHAT IS A LAUGHTER CLUB?

The word 'club' in the name is likely to convey the impression that a "Laughter Club" is like any other club as we know it. That is not so. A Laughter Club is nothing more than a group of people who want to laugh together, every morning, in the open, in a public place and do so. It has no formal structure and no office bearers, but just a couple of anchor persons who lead the group in laughter. There is no formal membership, no form to be filled in, no fee and no other fuss. You come and join the group, laugh with them and you are a member of the 'Laughter Club'. As simple as that.

Nowadays, Laughter Clubs are becoming popular all over India and there is great interest in such clubs from people all over the world. The reason being that many people have derived health benefits from this innovative concept. It seems that this laughter movement has the potential to become a global phenomenon. To evaluate the benefits of laughter on physical, mental and social health, it needs to be monitored and researched by medical experts. To make it more effective, laughter groups need to be trained in a scientific manner and there has to be a uniform format for a laughing session, without any diversions and irregularities. Now, the time has come when we need to structure the concept to make it more effective. Keeping this in mind we have formed a central body "Laughter Club International" and it will have affiliated clubs all over the world.

STEP I: SEARCH FOR THE RIGHT PLACE

If anyone wants to start a Laughter Club, find a place in your locality where people can assemble early in the morning when they go for a walk. It can be either a public park, an open ground or a beach. The advantage of selecting such a place is that you can combine laughter therapy sessions with your morning walk. Since it is group laughter, the more the people, the better the effects. It is easier to gather a large number of people at such places.

The chosen place should not be in the immediate vicinity of residential complexes so as to prevent any disturbance to others. In those areas where weather conditions are not favourable throughout the year it is not possible to have laughter sessions round the year. Under such circumstances these sessions can be held during yoga classes, at health clubs or at aerobic centers, where laughter can be a value addition to the ongoing activities.

There are many people who can't get up early in the morning and others who have to rush to their work places. They may not be able to attend laughter session. The ideal alternative for such people would be to have a laughter session at their offices, or factories, provided the management is convinced about the benefits of the concept. We have already started laughter sessions in many small factories in Mumbai and in one corporate house in Pune.

STEP II: REGISTRATION OF YOUR CLUB

For getting your club registered you may write to: The President, Laughter Club International Head Quarters, A-1, Denzil, 3rd Cross Road, Lokhandwala Complex, Andheri (W), Mumbai-400 053, (India). Tel: 022-631 6426 / Telefax: 022-632 4293, Email: Laugh@vsnl.com, to get a new club registration form along with an information guide. Form an Organising Committee consisting of 5 members who will be founder members and will be trained as anchor persons. Include one or two women if possible. Forms are to be submitted along with a one-time registration and affiliation fee (non-refundable) of US $1000, as a demand draft in the name of "Laughter Club International".

STEP-III

After acknowledgment of the registration, organise a group of at least 25-30 people (the larger the better) who would be participating in laughter sessions everyday. We will fix a date for the opening of the Laughter Club in your city. The registration fee should be collected by voluntary contributions from the participants, or by the organisation or company.

STEP: IV

To create awareness of the opening of the Laughter Club, banners or posters can be displayed 15-20 days before the opening ceremony. We can provide the design, logo, icon and matter for the banners and posters which can be suitably modified. Media people should be informed well in advance about the event and we can provide ready-made material for your press release. Media people love to cover Laughter Clubs. Local cable networks are ideal platforms for comprehensive coverage.

STEP: V

The Laughter Club International will organise a team of experts who will come to your area for a lecture and demonstration of various techniques of yogic laughter. They will also train your anchor persons who will be conducting laughter sessions everyday. Select only those persons as anchors who will be regularly attending the sessions and who are extroverts, who can give commands for various exercises, with confidence. The wrong selection of anchor persons will be counterproductive as they have to take charge of and start conducting the session from the very next day. On behalf of the Laughter Club International, we are also training the anchors as Laughter Therapists.

The expenses of conveyance, boarding and lodging of the team of experts will be borne by the organising group. The unique feature of Laughter Clubs is that there should be no membership fee for individuals. However, to promote the mission, commercial profit-making organisations can contribute some money as a voluntary donation from time to time. If members are wealthy they can also donate voluntarily to the cause, as such contributions are exempt from tax under 80 G.

If you can't afford the expenses of the team, you can approach social organisations like the Rotary or Lions, or corporate houses and philanthropists to sponsor the event in the public interest.

LAUGH LIKE
AN ARAB

CHAPTER - 22

Role of the Anchor Person in a Laughter Club

One of the absolute requirements of running a successful Laughter Club is having an anchor person or a ring leader. There can be more than one anchor person in a group. His job is not to crack jokes and make people laugh, nor he is supposed to do any mimicry or funny actions. His main purpose is to initiate the different stages of laughter, breathing exercises and stretching exercises. He is like a trigger, who laughs more easily and infectiously than others. His job is to motivate others to drop their inhibitions and be more playful, so that stimulated laughter can be converted into genuine peals of hilarity. Good self confidence, proper eye contact and a vibrant voice to give commands to initiate laughter are some of basic qualities he or she must have.

PROPER TRAINING

With all the inbuilt qualities of a good leader, the anchor person needs proper training to conduct a laughter session. Since yogic

laughter is a new concept, proper understanding of the subject is very necessary. Books and literature are available at the headquarters of the Laughter Club International. It is better to go through them before starting a Laughter Club. Being a new concept, people might ask many questions which need to be answered. On behalf of the Laughter Club International we keep holding anchor person training programmes from time to time. If the training course is done before starting a club it is much better. The first formal training is imparted to the anchor person at the time of the opening of the new club, when experts demonstrate the various types of stimulated laughter.

At that time, if the anchor person has a list of the different steps of a laughter session he can pick up the techniques very fast. Therefore, he must memorise the steps so as to practice various types of commands during the first training.

Important: At the time of opening a new Laughter Club, a proper anchor person should be selected. He/she should be very regular and should be able to conduct the session from the very next day.

Many clubs do not take off well because of the selection of the wrong anchor person.

How to Give a Command

The most important skill of an anchor person in a laughter session is to give commands to participants to initiate different types of laughter and other exercises. The basic purpose of giving a command is to make all the members of the group laugh at the same time. This helps to build up a good tempo of laughter and creates a good effect which stimulates others to laugh. In contrast, if different group members laugh with different tones and timings, it will not elicit a satisfactory response. The response of the group will depend upon the proper command and energy levels of the leader. Therefore, a leader should always be swift and full of energy. His voice should be audible and clear.

A typical laughter command is given by saying One....Two.... Three. It should be delivered slowly, loudly and building towards a crescendo, that is, with gradually increasing volume. For example you should say one in a normal tone, two should be little louder and t...h....r....eeeeee.... should be said with such gusto that all the members are stimulated to laugh at the same time, which has a good effect. To initiate deep breathing, all the participants should start at the same time because the timing of inspiration, holding the breath and expiration has to be monitored according to yogic principles. So, it is important to have all the members start at the same time. Therefore to initiate deep breathing the command should be: Now we'll take a deep breath.... Ready.... Start! The word start should be said a little, louder.

For stretching exercises, the commands are a little different. Normally, we do five rounds of each stretching exercise of the neck and shoulder. First one must name the exercise and then say one..... (slowly).....two............, ...three........., four........ and five. Members should be asked to do the exercise slowly and at the

172

end of the range of movement a pleasurable stretch should be maintained and then they come back to the starting position. The anchor person himself should should do it slowly to demonstrate the speed of the movement. If necessary the proper execution of exercises should be demonstrated from time to time for the benefit of new members. Instructing and correcting members during the session should be avoided. It might waste time and may cause embarrassment to the participant.

FORMATTING THE GROUP

Since *Hasya Yoga* (Laughter Yoga) is a dynamic exercise, what is very important, is how to make the group members stand and at what distance. Mostly people prefer to stand in a circle format with the anchor person in the middle. In this format the leader should keep turning around so as to keep eye contact with all the members. If the anchor is not turning in a circle, people standing behind him feel ignored or less motivated. Sometimes introvert and shy members would like to stand behind to evade the public eye. This will create hurdles in removing their inhibitions and in the proper execution of various laughter exercises. Another effective format is a semi-circle, where the anchor person stands at one end and maintains eye contact with all the members.

DISTANCE BETWEEN MEMBERS

This distance between members is very important. While doing stretching exercises we need more distance so that members do not touch each other with stretched arms. But, if the distance between the members is too much it will not allow proper eye contact between participants in order to convert stimulated laughter in to genuine giggles. Secondly, while laughing one should not be self-conscious about maintaining a distance from each other. Look into the other's eyes and laugh. Then one should move on to other member to share the laugh.

Therefore, according to the new model of a laughter therapy session, all the exercises along with deep breathing are done at the beginning of the session. It also allows more and more members who are a few minutes late to join in. Also, stretching exercises make participants more relaxed and less inhibited to do laughing exercises. Therefore, it is alright to maintain a distance between members initially, while doing exercises, but when starting with the first laughter exercise, the anchor should call all the members a little closer. Try to make it like a random group. There is no need to stand in a queue during a laughter session. In fact, members should be instructed to keep moving and changing their places, going up to different members and laughing with them. Standing steady in one particular place is a sign of inhibition and rigidity, which will affect the quality of laughter.

The varying distances and movements will help to bring in more playfulness, which will help to make the laughter session more spontaneous and enjoyable.

At the end of the session, the group members are asked to come still closer to do gradient laughter and to shout the laughter slogans. Gradient laughter is a most enjoyable and powerful type of laughter. It is much closer to spontaneous and meditative laughter. It can only be performed well if members are asked to come closer.

MOTIVATION LEVELS

To make people laugh without jokes is no laughing matter. It needs both skill and motivation levels to make laughter session more enjoyable. In addition to giving proper commands, the anchor person should be a good motivator. He should be able to inspire others to keep their spirits high. Therefore, the anchor person himself should be dynamic and full of energy. To keep the spirits high one should remember the philosophy of 'Motion creates Emotion'. If you act like an energetic man you will become one over a period of time.

With the repetitive actions of acting happy and energetic, it will become a part of your nature after sometime. Therefore, since charity starts from home, likewise to motivate others, get motivated yourself first.

To motivate others, anchor person should move around in the circle going up to different members and making hand gestures as if saying "Come on" "Come out". Also he should verbalise encouraging words like "Wonderful", "Very good", "First Class" etc. In between the laughter exercises he must say, "Relax! Relax!" to make people more comfortable. Lastly, to keep the self-interest motive intact, there must be continual innovations and introducing of new items as per the recommendations of our central research team. One should be open to introducing new things in place of less interesting old actions. Therefore, the anchors should stay in touch with the Laughter Club International headquarters through correspondence, telephone, fax, e-mail etc.

DISCIPLINE IN A LAUGHTER CLUB

One of the features of a successful anchor person is being able to maintain discipline about timings and duration of laughter sessions. The entire session should be short and sweet, not lasting for more than 20-25 minutes. One of the hallmarks of a Laughter Club is that it starts sharp on time. Even if there are very few people the clapping and Ho Ho Ha Ha must start without waiting for other members to arrive. Now, people set their watches at the onset of a laughter session. There are many reasons for this punctuality, one of them being that many members have to go to work. The anchor person can't afford to be late and he has to reach five minutes earlier than the scheduled time of a laughter session.

The word discipline does not mean regimentation or bossing. One of the beauties of a Laughter Club is that there are no compulsions or strict rules that one has to come everyday, or one has to reach on time. It is up to the member to decide whether he wants to come everyday, or twice a week, or occasionally as and when he wishes to do so. But if the laughter session is being introduced by an organisation then their rules have to be followed. Normally, in public parks we leave it entirely upto the member's discretion as to how many times he wants to attend. Our simple logic is, if the sessions are good and enjoyable why should people miss them?

The idea of maintaining discipline is to maintain orderliness, togetherness and harmony. We favour administration with love and not with force. Even if some member tries to disturb the harmony of the club he should be gently spoken to after the session is over. The anchor should avoid scolding or shouting at him in front of everybody during the session. Inspite of the best efforts, if some member hampers the smooth functioning of the club, the anchor is fully authorised to ban the offender's entry, not by law but by the consensus of the existing members of the group.

TRAINING CO-ANCHORS

Laughter must go on 30 days in a month, 365 days in a year. In case the main anchor is not available, there should be a couple of co-anchors who should be able to run the show effectively. In my experience, the best leaders are those who glorify others and get their recognition. Some anchors have the tendency to lead the show all by themselves, not allowing others to come forward and conduct the session.

If you find that new anchors are able to conduct the whole session effectively, start slowly by asking them to conduct exercises and deep breathing first and then go on to different laughter exercises. Another good idea is to conduct the entire session jointly by dividing various sets of laughter commands. And by doing so, you can always ask new people to come forward and start with giving one particular command first.

This will create very good harmony among the members and help more and more people achieve self-confidence. The Laughter Club of Mulund has created more than 30 anchors in a group of 80-100 members. More and more women should be encouraged to anchor the proceedings. This will remove stage fright and fear of public speaking and develop self-confidence. Allowing others to be anchors will help them to transform their personalities from introverts to extroverts. There are hundreds of such examples in Laughter Clubs, where some people who could not speak even a word in public earlier, now effectively anchor laughter sessions.

KEEP RELIGION AND POLITICS AWAY

We are dreaming of a unified world and of bringing about world peace through Laughter. On the basis of any religion we can never unite the world and bring communal harmony. Laughter belongs to everyone and it has the potential to become a common link between people of all religions, castes, creeds, colours, the rich and poor, boss and subordinate.

Different religions may help to achieve spiritual enlightenment through different religious practices, but laughter is one of the easiest and most acceptable forms of spirituality. We are taking the best of the wisdom from all religions and implementing it practically in Laughter Clubs to achieve health and happiness.

Laughter sessions are held early in the morning and that is the time people go to religious places and say prayers. In Laughter Clubs due to the beliefs of anchor persons, some prayers and chanting of religious hymns were introduced. Though it was liked by many members, this was harming the secular format of Laughter Clubs. This platform is open to all communities. However broad-minded a person may be, still you can't make him accept anything based on a particular religion. Prayers might not elicit the same devotion in the mind of a person belonging to another religion.

Therefore, it is the duty of an anchor person not to undertake any prayers or let anybody belonging to a particular religion take advantage of Laughter Clubs. In many clubs which had already started prayers I had to make very hard efforts to convince them to stop. I told them, prayer is a very personal thing and it should be done in a private place or a religious institution. Prayers are never said casually in a public place. I further told them that religions had always divided people and had sparked off communal violence all over the world.

Heeding my advice, many clubs have stopped prayers. Now before starting a new club instruction are given in advance. Another important instruction to anchor persons is, not to use a Laughter Club as a platform to invite politicians of any political party to speak. As far as possible, laughter should be free from politics. Care should be taken not to allow anyone to use a Laughter Club for political gains.

ORGANISING FUN GAMES, PICNICS, HEALTH CAMPS

In addition to laughter sessions in the mornings, most clubs are now organising outings, picnics and health camps. The expenses involved in these activities can be contributory. Family members, friends and relatives of regular member may be invited for such occasions. This is one way of marketing laughter and increasing the membership of your club. If the gatherings on such occasions are good, you can approach local banks, popular stores, companies or business houses to sponsor such events by putting up their banners to cover a part of the expenses.

ASSIST IN RESEARCH

From time to time we will be conducting medical research to evaluate the health benefits of laughter therapy. Anchor persons can help the research team in interviewing club members and getting the research proforma filled in. Even if some tests are be conducted, they will be entirely sponsored by the central body, the Laughter Club International.

IMPORTANT ANNOUNCEMENTS

The anchor person will act as a bridge between club members and the Laughter Club International. From time to time we will keep sending mailers about various activities, research findings, new developments and different projects to bring good health and happiness to members. We will also send information about various national and international conferences on laughter and humour. With the help of behaviour scientists from all over the world, we will help Laughter Club members to overcome negative emotions like fear, anger, guilt, jealousy etc. At present we have designated Monday as 'Compliment Day' and Friday as 'Forgiveness Day' to help members bring about inner happiness. Anchor persons will keep making announcements to implement these programmes. If necessary, copies can be made and distributed among the members.

HEALTH WATCH

Anchors will keep a watch on various club members asking them about their welfare from time to time. Once a fortnight, an announcement should be made to inform the members about who should not participate in laughter sessions. For example, any one having angina problem (chest pain), hernia, glaucoma, cough with sputum for more than 10 days, acute viral infections (cold, flu), uterovaginal prolapse and slipped disc problems with back pain, should consult their doctors before attending a laughter session. If any person feels any discomfort during a session he should consult his doctor before joining the next session. Any elderly person with complaints of giddiness should get himself checked by his doctor.

For hygienic reasons, a pack of tissues should be kept in case someone gets phlegm while laughing. Members should be discouraged from spitting in the open. Anchors will also keep a watch on those members who are over-exerting during the session.

IRREGULARITIES AND CHANGE OF FORMAT

With the growing popularity of the laughter movement, many groups have started laughter sessions on their own, without proper training. This might cause some harm as the sessions should be monitored by medical experts. We also encourage the clubs to keep experimenting with new ideas to create playfulness and fun in Laughter Clubs. But some leaders try to change the existing laughter exercises according to their own judgement. If the main exercises are not standardised, it becomes difficult to do medical research to evaluate which particular exercise is more beneficial and which is less. It has also been observed that according to the liking of some anchors, various types of new exercises are introduced which significantly reduce the duration of laughter exercises, as the total duration of the whole session is 20-25 minutes.

If a particular group wants to introduce more exercises or other items, should be done before the scheduled time or after the laughter session is over. Extra exercises should not be a compulsion for all the members. If certain types of laughter or exercises are liked by a particular group other than the standard format, they should not exceed 5 minutes.

WELCOME NEW MEMBERS

It is a tradition in many clubs to call first-time visitors into the center and give them welcome laughter. Similarly if a member of any other club from the same city or from outstation happens to visit your club, he must be acknowledged and honoured. This will motivate many new members to join your club.

ATTENDING SEMINARS AND CONFERENCES

Periodically we will hold seminars and conferences to share new ideas from experts on laughter and humour and behaviour scientists from around the world. The leaders and co-anchors must attend these sessions to gain new insights and implement innovative concepts. During health workshops and yoga and meditation camps, anchor persons must take the opportunity to call a few members and share their experiences with Laughter Therapy.

HEALTH CAUTIONS FOR ANCHOR PERSONS

One of most important precautions every leader must take is, not to overstrain voice. In order to motivate the group members, leaders have to make extra efforts which can sometimes put an unnecessary strain on the body. Most vulnerable are the vocal cords which may develop nodules, which may lead to permanent hoarseness. Utmost care should be taken not to put extra strain on any part of the body while giving demonstrations/commands during laughter sessions.

LAUGH LIKE
A GENIE

LAUGH LIKE
A GOTH

CHAPTER - 23

World Laughter Day World Peace Thru' Laughter

Today, we are on the brink of nuclear disaster and wide spread international terrorism. More and more countries are acquiring nuclear capabilities. Having nuclear bombs is not a guarantee of peace, as thought by many top leaders of the world. If one mad man presses the button, others will have to respond. Why is there so much unrest in the world these days?

We are at war within ourselves, that is why there is war outside in the world today. If we can bring peace inside us through Laughter Clubs, by doing yogic laughter and practising ways and means of sensible living in a group and these small groups multiply all over the world, there will be everlasting peace in the entire world. Laughter is a powerful positive emotion. It creates a positive aura around individuals. When a group of individuals laughs together, it creates a collective community aura. Electromagnetic waves from a group who are laughing every day, form a protective envelope around that area to protect it from evil forces. Similarly, people believed in older days that one saintly person was enough to protect the entire village. If these laughter groups multiply all over the country it will change the consciousness of the entire nation.

Similarly, having Laughter Clubs all over the world can build up a global consciousness of brotherhood and friendship. To spread the message of world peace through Laughter Clubs all over the world we have decided to celebrate World Laughter Day on the second Sunday of every January, when thousands of people would gather to laugh together at a public place or a stadium.

Normally any world event should be so designated by the United Nations to get international support. We thought getting United Nations approval at this stage might be difficult as it is a new organisation and we still have to build up international consensus and prove our bonafides by conducting some more research before the world community accepts it. It was only to bring about more awareness internationally that our central body, the Laughter Club International decided to celebrate the event on the second Sunday of every January. Ideally, we should start the new year with laughter only. But people hardly sleep on the night of December 31st, so it was difficult to have gatherings on the 1st morning. Since the first Sunday might fall too close to 1st January the second Sunday was the best choice. Ultimately, if we are thinking of making it an international event, the month of January is freezing in half of the world. We are thinking of shifting World Laughter Day to the month of April or May when more and more countries can join in and laugh together.

FIRST WORLD LAUGHTER DAY

The 11th day of January, 1998, went down in history, when more than 10,000 members from Laughter Clubs all over India and a few

Laughter Happy-demic : No Jokes! They all came for a Mega Laugh. More than ten thousand people attended the World Laughter Day celebrations at Shivaji Park Mumbai on 10th January 1999.

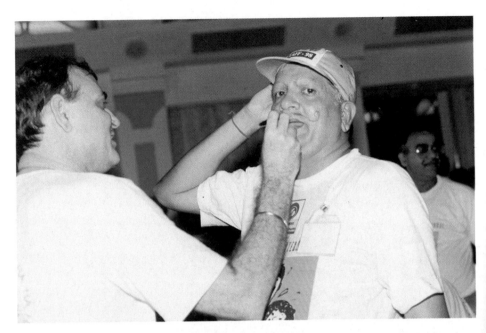

Nearly 800 Men and Women precipitated in a Moustache Drawing Competition

**"World Peace through Laughter" was the slogan during
first All India Laughter Convention-LAFF-98 held at Goa in Septemember 1998**

"Women power" in Laughter Clubs

A Leading Gynacologist among the percipients

invitees from other countries assembled and laughed together at the race course grounds, Mahalaxmi, Mumbai, to tell the entire world that we need to take laughter seriously. The enthusiastic participation by thousands of members has proved that these Laughter Clubs are not a laughing matter. The grounds which are usually filled with the sound of horses galloping, the groans of many losers and the laughter of a few winners, perhaps for the first time, reverberated with laughter and happiness.

To participate in the celebrations, members of various clubs along with their nears and dear ones, arrived at Worli Seaface, overlooking the vast expanse of the Arabian Sea, in about a hundred buses at 7 a.m. in the morning. The participants dressed in white, wearing laughter logo caps and holding colourful banners, were bubbling with energy with smiles on their faces. Placards read "World Peace Thru' Laughter", "Join a Laughter Club, It's Free", I am a Laughter Club Member," etc. A four kilometer `Peace March' was flagged off with chanting of Ho Ho Ha Ha Ha and frequent bouts of voluntary group laughter. It looked as if they could not possibly wait to convey to the world, the message, that laughter elevates people's minds, raises their spirits, improves their health, enhances their well being, brings them closer and unites them. Laughter could, therefore, also unite nations and bring about world peace. Recognising the importance of the occasion, the press, TV and other mediamen were present in large numbers.

In addition to international media agencies like Reuters, ANI and AFP, a full-fledged TV team from the Republic of Korea had come specially to cover the celebrations and the Consul-General of Korea graced the occasion as a Guest of Honour. When the procession reached the entrance of the race course grounds, members were greeted with the beating of traditional drums and everybody danced to the beat of the well-known Punjabi *Bhangra* dance. As most participants were in white clothes, the length of the procession within the compound, upto the central stage looked like the serpentine flow of a milky river. There were no chairs, except those on the stage, and, be it said to the credit of participants, they happily sat down on the ground. Together, they looked, from a distance, like a sea of enthusiastic faces with the glow of smiles matching that of the atmosphere.

To begin the session, the Navy band injected some music into the proceedings. The Chief Guest, Nana Chudasma, former Sheriff of Mumbai, and Mr. Bong Koo Rhee, the Consul General of the Republic of Korea, and other dignitaries were seated on the dais. After brief introductory speech, colourful balloons were released and then came the electrifying moment when I, along with my wife Madhuri, conducted 10 minutes of group laughter. It was a dream come true for me. I had always dreamt of gathering thousands of people and having a mega laughter session. A well known music director, Kalyanjibhai, along with his band of very talented young children "Little Wonders" sang a theme song on laughter, composed specially for the occasion - *"Haste Raho aur Hasati Raho"* meaning, keep laughing and also keep making others laugh. That same evening the event appeared on many television channels and photographs of the laughter - the happydemic appeared in many national and international news papers.

THE SECOND MEGA EVENT

The second World Laughter Day kicked off happily on 10th January, 1999, at 7.30 am at Shivaji Park grounds in the heart of Mumbai. This time too, more than 10,000 members from all over country gathered on one of the coldest Sundays of the season. We held a two-kilometre Peace March with dancing, the beating of a variety of drums, shouting slogans and repeated bouts of group laughter. Hundreds of school children also took part in the Peace March in their uniforms. We hope to celebrate the next World Laughter Day outside India to welcome the beginning of the next millineum with laughter.

190

CALL FOR A UNIFIED WORLD

Through the Laughter Club movement we want to remind the whole world that human beings are the only species who is blessed by the Almighty with the gift of laughter. Today we have forgotten to laugh and there is an urgent need to take laughter seriously. Laughter is a universal language which has the potential to unite humanity without a particular religion. Laughter is a neo-religion which can establish a common link between various religions and create a new world order. The idea sounds over-ambitious, but these are the vibrations I am getting from the Creator. Yes! It is laughter and only laughter which can unite the world.

WHY NOT LAUGHTER IN THE OLYMPICS?

On the occasion of the second World Laughter Day we strongly recommended the introduction of a 'Laughter Contest' during the Olympics. In fact the opening day should start with a laughter session by athletes from all over the world and viewers should join them.

I am willing to give them training. Is anybody listening? The idea of a Laughter Contest at the Olympics was coined by a young Indian boy in 1995. Just before the Atlanta Olympics, one of three lads who qualified for Visa Olympics of the Imagination (VOIs) a future Olympic sport was Nirmal John from India. The contest asked children aged between 11 and 13 years to create their own vision of a new Olympic sport and to describe how their new sport would promote world peace and unity. The young Indian proposed that a Laughter Contest should be included in the Olympics, because it would certainly promote world peace.

It would bring down tension among the nations and help to attain everlasting peace. Nirmal John's artwork depicted five persons (representing five countries, of different races, including a woman) taking part in a laughter contest.

The Laughter Club International is a non-religious, non-parochial and non-commercial organisation. We are committed to spreading the message of good health, friendship and brotherhood all over the world. In our future plans we are introducing laughter at work places, schools and colleges, during competitive sports, at old age homes, in destitute women groups, in prisons, orphanages and blind institutes, on ships and for the police, army, navy and air force. World Laughter Day on 10th January, 1999, was also celebrated in Germany, where hundreds of members participated in group laughter conducted by Mr Heinz Tobler who took training from me while he was in Mumbai last year. Mr. Steve Wilson, America's Joyologist also conducted a laughter session with 150 professionals in Columbus (Ohio) U.S.A., to mark the occasion.

LAUGH LIKE A ROMAN EMPEROR

CHAPTER - 24

Research in Laughter Therapy

L aughter is as old as mankind itself and its benefits have been felt for centuries. Everybody understands that laughter is beneficial and relaxing. But, it is only recently that the scientific basis of the benefits of laughter has been established. This chapter analyses the scientific principles of the medical benefits of laughter therapy, on the basis of research work done by many scientists all over the world and some of the clinical data gathered from Laughter Clubs in India.

LAUGHTER AS PRACTISED BY US

Laughter as practised by us is different from laughter therapy practised in the Western world. They have hospital-based-laughter clinics for individuals patients who are made to laugh by reading jokes or viewing comic videos. Our laughter is unprovoked, spontaneous group laughter by healthy individuals which works as a preventive health measure.

LAUGHTER AS AN EUSTRESS OR STRESS BUSTER

Hans Selye described laughter as a form of Eustress. This means that it is a positive, life enhancing type of stress. Laughter has a built-in balancing mechanism that encourages the two-step action of stimulation and relaxation due to the release of the chemicals adrenaline and noradrenaline. This produces a feeling of well-being by relieving the minor stresses and strains of daily life. Laughter reduces anxiety, tension and depression. Thus, it helps in mitigating several serious diseases such as hypertension, heart disease, diabetes, etc. in which anxiety and tension are predisposing factors. Kay Herth *(American Journal of Nursing 1984)* has documented reduction of hypertension after laughter therapy. Many of our members have reaped the beneficial effects of laughter in reducing hypertension, heart disease, diabetes, anxiety, insomnia, etc.

LAUGHTER AND HEALING

Laughter releases catecholamines together with adrenaline and noradrenaline. This enhances blood flow, reduces inflammation, speeds the healing process and heightens the overall arousal of the body. Thus it would help in mitigating arthritis, spondylitis, myofascitis and such other inflammatory diseases.

LAUGHTER AS AN ANALGESIC

Laughter releases two neuropeptides viz. Endorphins and Enkephalins. These are opioids which are the body's natural pain suppressing agents. The ability of laughter to release muscle tension and to soothe the sympathetic nervous system also helps to control pain, as does increased circulation. Thus, laughter has a multipronged approach for the relief of pain, in conditions such as arthritis, spondylitis, etc. This is aptly demonstrated by the famous article of Norman Cousins *(New England Journal of Medicine,* Dec 1976) where he documents that 10 minutes of laughter had an analgesic effect for 2 hours in his personal problem of severe ankylosing spondylitis. Cogan et al *(Journal of Behavioural Medicine* 1987) had demonstrated by clinical experiments that discomfort thresholds were higher in subjects after bouts of laughter. Some (21%) of our members with painful orthopaedic conditions have obtained relief.

LAUGHTER AND IMMUNITY

Lee S. Berk *(Clinical Research* 1989) had found that laughter may attenuate some stress related hormones and modify natural killer cell activity resulting in immunomodulation. Labott also supports Berk's findings *(Journal of Behavioural Medicine* 1990) and concludes that laughter results in improved immunity. In a study at Canada's University of Waterloo *(Well Being Journal),* it was well documented that laughter increases the levels of immunoglobulin IgA and IgG. Norman Cousins (*Prevention* March 1988) also states that laughter serves as a blocking agent against disease.

Thus laughter, by improving body immunity, can mitigate a host of chronic diseases such as bronchitis, the common cold, rheumatoid arthritis, allergies, etc. Improving immunity may also be a supplementary measure in the control of AIDS. Some (12.9%) of our members recorded improvements in such chronic diseases as bronchitis, common cold, etc.

CANCER AND LAUGHTER

In Berk and Tan's (1996) experiment concerning the laughter immune connection, they used few healthy fasting males who volunterred for the experiment and had them view a one hour funny video. They took blood samples of their interferon-gamma (IFN) before, during and after they watched the tape. They had significant results which showed increased activity in IFN after watching the funny video and on till the following day. IFN activates the CT-Cells, B-Cells immunoglobulins and Natural Killer Cells(NK).

This could be very important research for cancer since laughter also fights against tumour cells. Laughter's ability to be a pain reliever and it's ability to fight tumour cells have added an exciting new area in cancer research. Some of the research done by Carl Simonton and Stephaine Matthews-Simonton (1978) leads us to believe that a person's emotional status does indeed affect his likelihood of getting or overcoming cancer.

In our Laughter Clubs there are many cancer patients who are leading much healthier lives due to a positive attitude towards life. This makes us believe that laughter can be used as a preventive measure against cancer.

LAUGHTER AS AN AEROBIC EXERCISE

Dr. W. Fry states that laughter is a good aerobic exercise. He says that 100 laughs a day are equal to 10 minutes of rowing or jogging. Lloyd (*Journal of General Psychology* 1938) showed that laughter is a combination of deep inhalation and full exhalation, inspiring excellent ventilation, wonderful rest and profound release. Thus, laughter increases the lungs' vital capacity and oxygenation. We measured the lungs' vital capacity (peak flow rate) of our members using a Spirometer. The peak flow rate was lower than normal 13%, (< 300l/m.) it was normal in 67% (300-500 l/m.) and high in 20% (> 500l/m.). This would benefit patients with pulmonary diseases such as bronchitis, bronchial asthma, bronchiectasis, ect. Some (7.8%) of our members have gained relief in such lung disease.

LAUGHTER - A HOLISTIC APPROACH

Laughter has positive holistic benefits to normal healthy individuals such as improved concentration, better performance in examinations (Sobina White 1987), improved stamina in sportsmen and better performance by actors and singers. It increases self-confidence, improves interpersonal relationships and is also a simple method of meditation. All these benefits have been aptly demonstrated by a large majority of our members who are otherwise healthy individuals.

RESEARCH ON SCHIZOPHRENIC PATIENTS

Gelkopt, Kreitler and Sigal (1995) researched the effects of humour on hospitalised schizophrenic patients. Although they did not record any negative findings (mostly no change at all), they did have positive results. They took 34 schizophernic patients and showed them 70 video films within one month's time.

The control group watched humorous video films. There was a significant change in their aggressive behaviour. They were observed to have less verbal hostility and fewer psychiatric symptoms such as depression and anxiety. The results were not very significant because schizophrenic patients may be unable to recognise humour.

RESEARCH SURVEY IN INDIA

In India laughter has been in use as a therapeutic exercise and research interest has gradually increased, focussing on this aspect. A few survey studies have been conducted by Sheetal Agarwal that highlight the perceived therapeutic effects of laughter therapy.

Due to several limitations, other more sophisticated forms of research such as experimental research have not been conducted. But an adequate consolation is that we are moving towards accumulating more and more scientific evidence that validates the use of laughter as an effective form of therapy. Here are some of the physiological parameters of the research survey.

Parameter	% of Survey Population	% Who Perceive Improvement
Regular Walkers	97.56	86.25
Diabetes	13.4	9
Blood pressure	31.7	26.9
Respiratory problems	17.0	14.2
Heart Disease	7.3	33.3
Quality of sleep	57.3	65.8

It is important to note that a significant percentage of people suffering from heart disease perceived betterment after joining Laughter Clubs, especially pertaining to a reduction in chest pains.

PSYCHOLOGICAL MEASURES:

Coping better with anxiety and feelings of depression 19.5%

Coping better with stress   69.5%

Increased social interaction   74.39%

Noticeable change in mood and attitude   79.6%

With reference to psychological measures, the data available suggests a comparatively greater perceived effect. This is very evident in terms of participants of laughter therapy finding themselves coping better with stress. Though it has to be further studied as to how laughter therapy affects the individual's appraisal process in terms of a stressful situation, in a way that enables him to deal with stress more effectively. Also, it will be interesting to study for what kind of stresses laughter therapy is most effective.

The results also suggest an increase in the participants' level of social interaction. This, in more ways than one, provides for the psychological well being of the individual.

Participants of laughter therapy also find a marked change in their moods, as well as an attitudinal change. Finding themselves to be more positive in their outlook is a common experience for many of them, shown as a high percentage i.e. 79.26%, in the study.

98.7% of the participants find the format of laughter therapy adequate in terms of time and the structure of exercises.

Hence, it can be concluded that though much more structured procedures of research need to be implemented to assess the effects of laughter therapy, this study is a stepping stone in unravelling the basic effects perceived by the patients.

Clinical Analysis of 516 Members of Laughter Clubs from all over India

This study was conducted by Dr. Siddhartha D. Khandwala, M.D. (Bom.,) who is the anchor person of the Priyadarshani Laughter Club, Mumbai. Most members (71.7%) were males and in the age group of 50 to 70 years (63.5%) and retired individuals or housewives (40.2%) as senior citizens are more interested in such activities. However, almost 10% were younger people. It is necessary to target younger people and students, as well as women.

This movement has started only recently and still almost 40% of its members have been attending it for over a year. It is most heartening to note that 93.8% of members are regular participants, indicating the popularity of laughter sessions.

A majority (59.3%) of members are suffering from some ailment as would be expected in this age group. However, it is surprising to note that such simple laughter therapy has resulted in amelioration of the ailment in as many as 83.6%. The amelioration was of a moderate to substantial degree in 56.1%. It was heartening to note that 44% needed less medication and there was not a single case of worsening of the disease.

The holistic benefits of Laughter therapy are well documented and have recorded a positive improvement in members' general health both mental and physical. The attitude of a majority (82.6%) of members towards their family members improved, resulting in a more harmonious family life. 71.7% of members reported an improved relationship with their colleagues in their profession, business or place of service. Self confidence was increased in 85.7%, while 66.7% reported increased concentration.

Almost all (99.6%) stated that they would like to continue laughter sessions as well as recommend the same to others.

Many members reported several additional tangible benefits such as feeling energetic and fresh (31.1%); an improved outlook on life (11.2%); improved social behaviour and contacts (8.5%); increased stamina (3.9%); increased appetite and improved digestion (3%). All these minor benefits go towards improving the quality of life.

CONCLUSION

Thus, laughter has several medical/social/holistic benefits which can improve the quality of life substantially. Laughter can help to mitigate several diseases, some of them quite serious. Laughter is a "Stress Buster" and helps to relieve anxiety and tension which are the predisposing factors for several diseases. Laughter every day can keep the doctor away at no cost.

CHAPTER - 25

Laughter Club International

L aughter Club International(LCI) is a Worldwide organi sation, registered under the Societies Registration Act 1860. It also has a Public Trust exemption from tax under section 80G.

The LCI was formed in 1997 with the help of our visonary Senior Vice President **J.K. Kapur** and dynamic leader, Vice President **Mohit Kapoor** from the Worli Laughter Club. We are also grateful to **G.P.Shethia, B.P. Hirani** and **Kamini Bathija** for making our dream come true.

AIMS AND OBJECTIVES

❖ Our aim is to create awareness of this new yogic technique of Laughter Therapy all over India and other parts of the world, by setting up more Laughter Clubs and imparting practical training in various techniques of laughter. Thus, we can help to cultivate the spirit of laughter by understanding ways and means of sensible living and putting them in to practice through laughter.

❖ Our aim is to set up a team of doctors from various specialities and systems of medicine to conduct scientific studies and research work as to how laughter can affect the physical, mental, social and spiritual well being of the participants.

❖ Our aim is to publish journals and set up libraries of books, video cassettes, CDs and other information on Laughter Therapy.

❖ Our aim is to bring people of various countries together and bring everlasting peace through laughter.

❖ The outstanding feature of Laughter Clubs is that there is no membership fee. Laughter is absolutely free!

Affiliation to Laughter Club International: With the popularity of laughter therapy many people have started Laughter Clubs on their own. They are conducting Laughter sessions without proper training. Laughter Therapy is being supervised by a team of doctors and yoga experts who are undertaking research so as to bring the maximum benefits of Laughter Therapy to participants. If done in a wrong manner, or without proper training, it may not be effective or may even be harmful, if there is forceful laughter and exercise.

Under the new concept, we laugh in a group without taking the help of any jokes. To make it more spontaneous, keep the self interest motive intact and avoid boredom, laughter techniques need to be more stimulating. Our panel of experts will keep your Laughter Therapy programme updated from time to time.

The Laughter Club International is a worldwide organisation and by affiliation you well get the privilege of being a part of a big laughter family. We are starting inter-club exchange programmes, where members of one Laughter Club can visit other clubs in all cities of the country and abroad. A few member delegates will visit other cities with prior intimation and you will be provided home stay with the members of Laughter Clubs. The host club will arrange to visit various clubs in that particular city, along with sight seeing.

We are planning to start extensive medical research on various aspects of physical, mental and spiritual health. We are expecting funding of these research projects by national and international organisations and the benefit of medical research will be passed on to all the affiliated clubs. We are also planning a computerised health file for all Laughter Club members in the near future.

MEDICAL INFORMATION

All the affiliated members will get the latest information about club activities all over the world, as well as regular newsletters and other research material on laughter therapy, yoga and health building activities.

The Laughter Club International will conduct regular training programmes on meditation, yoga, personality development, healthy eating and sensible living. These workshops and seminars will be organised periodically and all the affiliated clubs will get information.

Laughter Clubs are no more a laughing matter. They are being recognized by social organisations, corporate houses and other industries. Hotels are offering massive discounts on picnics organised by Laughter Clubs and many companies are offering discounts to Laughter Club members. We are planning to issue a "Laughter Card" to members of affiliated clubs. At present more than 500 establishments are willing to offer a discount to Laughter Card holders.

GUIDELINES FOR AFFILIATED CLUBS

1. The Laughter Club International is a registered organisation under the Societies Registration Act 1860 and is also registered as a Public Trust with 80G facility for tax exemption. For affiliation to the Laughter Club International (LCI), get the name of your club registered by paying 1000 U.S. dollars (out of India)

in favour of the Laughter Club International (LCI). A club registration number along with receipt and affiliation certificate will be issued. The registration fee will be managed by voluntary contributions from the Organising Committee members who wish to start the club.

2. The Organising Committee will have at least 5 and a maximum of 9 members, out of which 2-3 members should be women. One person will be a group leader, nominated by consensus, who will be known as the Chairman and others will be all members-cum-anchor persons. Don't create any posts or levels, as there will be no elections for the committee members. In case a particular club fails to find a leader, the committee members will be nominated by the Laughter Club International.

3. Laughter Club members should not undertake any social work which needs collection of funds from club members or outside the club.

4. All the affiliated clubs will get information letters and newsletters, from the LCI with a nominal subscription amount. The LCI will also hold workshops, seminars, national and international conferences from time to time. The Governing Council of the Laughter Club International will decide the recurring costs of such material to be supplied to the club members. The costs will change from time to time and the amount will be generated by voluntary contributions.

5. Affiliated clubs may print letterheads carrying the LCI logo with standard colour and design. The letterhead must carry the name of the Founder President Dr. Madan Kataria, followed by Organising Committee members. All the certificates, badges, awards and mementos will have the logo of the LCI.

6. Affiliated clubs shall not open any new branch without approval and proper registration with the LCI - the central body.

Laughter session among school children

Laughter session with blind was a memorable exeperience.

Laughter session at Parimal Garden Ahmedabad (Gujrat)

Laughter Club of Lokhandwala Complex : The birth place of Laughter Movement

Laughter Competition in progress at Priyadarshani park

Mr. P. T. Hinduja "Best Laughing Man" of year 1999.

7. The club shall not make any major changes in the format of standard laughter and exercises which are periodically fixed by the central body.

8. The club should function on a non-religious, non-parochial and non-political basis. No prayers relating to a particular religion should be introduced in Laughter Clubs.

9. Membership is free to all the citizens on this earth. Anybody may join a Laughter Club anywhere in the world, provided the person is not hampering the smooth functioning of the club. Though there is no membership fee, all the members are required to fill the entrance form to maintain records and carry out research work.

10. If required by the central body (LCI) for promotion and fund raising all the affiliated clubs will display banners, placards and other advertising materials provided by the central body during laughter sessions, regional conferences, picnics and annual gatherings.

11. At least one or two anchor persons must attend zonal or central body meetings, whenever necessary.

CHAPTER - 26

Criticism of the Laughter Club

Ever since I initiated the first Laughter Club, there has been plenty of good news about the novelty of the concept, thanks to the media all over the world. For quite some time, there was not even a single journalist who criticized it. It was sometime later, that a few critical comments started appearing in newspapers. However, in the beginning, I used to hear a few comments from onlookers, "Laughter is something natural, how can one force laughter?" Even a few entrants initially expressed scepticism about the quality of laughter but revised their views after some experience saying: "Oh! It is relaxing. I never thought it would be so good."

It is also true that a majority of the people who come for a walk don't join the laughter group. The reasons could be many. One, their inhibitions, the common block in most cases. Two, they are not aware that many of the benefits claimed for laughter have been authenticated by scientific research.

Some opine that this club is meant only for those who do not laugh at all. They think they themselves laugh enough throughout the day and, therefore, they need not join the club. Though they are amused by the concept, they feel that they have better things to do.

GOOD CRITICISM

There were a number of individuals who, after seeing a couple of Laughter Clubs and reading through magazines and newspapers, started laughing on their own, not following standard techniques formulated by the Laughter Club International. The result was that those participating in such groups found the exercise monotonous and boring until they joined a properly constituted Laughter Club.

Somewhere in the middle of 1996, a senior surgeon happened to attend one of the sessions in a suburb of Mumbai. He found that many people, in their enthusiasm, applied too much force while laughing. Obviously, he thought this was not the right way and such an increase in intra-abdominal pressure might cause herniation. Secondly, he also objected to laughing with the mouth closed. He opined that it might push an infection from the throat into the middle ear. Technically he is right, but we have not had a single case with such a problem. I used to regularly emphasise the importance of avoiding strain stating that could be harmful and could also take away the spontaniety from their laughter, but, evidently, over-enthusiasm got the better of some. The surgeon's criticism appeared in a popular evening newspaper and was all for the good as many of those who read it corrected their techniques.

I am a born optimist and continue to think that people who criticize you, are your real friends and help you to improve upon your shortcomings. The first critical article appeared in the *Bombay Times* in April 1997, written by a lady journalist who happened to stay near a Laughter Club where a handful of senior citizens laughed every day, after chanting a few religious hymns on a beach. When she first heard the sounds of laughter, she, somehow, found them disturbing early in the morning and felt prompted to write her critical comments based merely on her observations from the balcony. I wish she had done so after participating in a couple of sessions. I have had a journalist coming from overseas after travelling thousands of miles, to actually experience the Laughter Club and then write about it.

But this was, I believe, the first journalist who wrote an article without experiencing the laughter which she could have done so easily. She believed, she said, that there must be something to laugh at, only then could it be beneficial laughter. She thought laughter was not a commodity which could be practised and perfected and added that fake and forced laughter makes you feel foolish and it is a painful procedure. She thought the world had gone crazy. First came synthetic tears, then fake organs, and how could even a natural emotion like laughter be processed artificially? I chose not to offer any explanation as I felt that the article was based more on writing skill than a result of actual experience.

I wish she had visited a couple of Laughter Clubs before expressing criticism in the article. I wish she could have seen people practicing deep breathing in between various types of laughter. I wish she could have met a couple of patients of depression, who had reduced their pill intake and had become cheerful.

I wish she could have seen them gather together like one family and share each other's sorrows and joys. At least once she could have attended a birthday celebration at a Laughter Club, seen fun games being played and seen the spirit of laughter flowing out of the member's whole beings, rather than their laughing occasionally while watching a comedy show.

Similarly, another so-called 'laughter lover', saw Laughter Clubs as "The Death of Laughter", as he described them in his article. He called Laughter Club members 'tired middle-aged cynics, urban hyenas of a concrete jungle, laughing without jokes', and, according to him, this was plastic and synthetic laughter, like having an orgasm without sex, like sex without love, etc. Undoubtedly, every one is free to express his or her views, even if critical. But, I am sure, those who do so will also agree that criticism, if better informed, will be more constructive.

MEDICAL COMMUNITY

In the begining, there were harsh reactions from the medical community. In general, doctors seemed somewhat uneasy about the laughter concept. Though not denying desirablity of creating a positive attitude, they could not bring themselves round to support this new type of therapy. I was initially invited to give a talk at the Indian Medical Association in two cities, but must confess I could not create much impact.

One fine day, I was handed a circular from a Medical Association in the suburbs of Mumbai, about their monthly meeting. It had an interesting agenda:

1. How to bring fun and happiness in life?

2. How to ban Laughter Clubs?

The reason for banning laughter clubs given was that they were spreading tuberculosis. They thought right. Tuberculosis is, in fact, rampant in India and open cases of tuberculosis could spray out tubucular germs. But what they overlooked was that Laughter Clubs are well organised and supervised by medical experts and that the members belong to a group of health-conscious people who are doctors, engineers, businessmen, chartered accountants etc. But this incident made us more alert about screening anyone with a persistent cough for more than seven days. By the grace of God, not even a single case of tuberculosis has been reported in more than 20,000 laughter club members all over the country. Instead, they have improved their resistance power and have fewer attacks of coughs and colds than ever before. We have also been advising members with severe colds to avoid attending the Laughter Club for the first couple of days.

I may also mention that over a period of time, the position has changed and there are more medical people who are now Laughter Club members. Evidently, scepticism has changed to conviction about the benefits of a Laughter Club.

LAUGH LIKE A CHINESE EMPEROR

CHAPTER - 27

World Laughter Tour
East meets West
through Laughter

The idea of a world laughter tour emerged when Steve Wilson, a clinical and industrial psychologist met me in Mumbai. He was very much impressed with the new idea of laughter clubs. We discussed for long hours about western and eastern philosophies of laughter and humor. In the West, laughter and its physiological correlates are well documented, but often studied in terms of reaction to the cognitive function of humour. A well- established western philosophy might be described as "Know yourself". Whereas a well established eastern philosophy might be described as "Become yourself". This difference shows up in the East-West approaches to laughter. For one thing, the western approach to laughter seems to seek research data and `evidence' of the power of laughter, where the eastern thinking is often "we have been doing this for 5000 years so we already know it works. If we are happy you can judge from our faces and you don't have to give evidence for the happiness.'' Most humour educators in the west are taking their lessons into the work place to help employees stay healthy, happy and productive, while others are using the information to help people just enjoy life more and applying the science of laughter to medicine, health and healing.

In India, laughter is being practised by healthy individuals to prevent sickness and to some extent we are using group laughter as a therapeutic measure to reduce stress. The most striking feature of Laughter Clubs is the use of laughter for social transformation, especially when linked with concepts of sensible living. Here the emphasis is not on humour and developing a sense of humour, it is about the act of laughter, which when done in large groups, has what appears to be a 'naturally humorous' outcome: simulated laughter really does become stimulated laughter. The western approach may be described in latin as 'gelosmedici' (laughter as medicine) and the eastern approach as 'gelospopuli' (Laughter of the people). The point is that both are needed.

The time has come to travel all over the world to search out all related practices and then synthesize them into teachings that expand the repertoire of laughter practitioners everywhere. There is zeigeist now about laughter and smiling 'without jokes'. Zeitgeist is the term that sociologists use to describe the phenomenon of simultaneous appearance of a certain invention around the world because the time is just right for it. In the West, people have long advocated, finding lots of reasons to laugh (the importance of a good sense of humour). They have traditionally silenced some laughers by challenging them to explain what's so funny! Now, here is an idea from the East - we can laugh for no reason. We are on our way to blending the two approaches so that we should laugh for no reason as well as for every reason and perhaps for the best reason, because we can!

What is the World Laughter Tour?

The world has forgotten how to laugh. Much of the world does not yet know about the proven benefits of laughter and humour. Yet, around the world there are people developing ways and means to use humour and laughter for health, peace, productivity and to enhance joy of living. We wish to network these people and make their work more visible and share new ideas to make this earth a better place for living.

The World Laughter Tour (WLT) is the brainchild of Steve Wilson, who teamed up with Karyn Buxman and me. Steve Wilson is a clinical and industrial psychologist, America's popular joyologist, an international speaker and frequent consultant to business houses around the world. He is an author who has written many books to promote the benefits of humor laughter and playfulness. Karyn Buxman, is a past-president of the American Association for Therapeutic Humor (AATH) and a full-time professional speaker concentrating on bringing the healing power of humour and laughter to health professionals as well as business organisations.

WLT is a grassroot movement with the mission of bringing events that promote health and peace through laughter and humor to every continent, through education. On the first leg of the American World Laughter Tour I am joining them in the month of May1999, to visit 8-10 major cities in the United States. After the American tour there is interest in bringing the WLT to England, Australia, Italy, Germany, Switzerland, Singapore, Japan and many other countries all over the world.

What Happens When the WLT hits Your Town?

We will be teaming up to present professional development workshops and public seminars to learn about the extra-ordinary connection between laughter and health with a twist: the East meets West through laughter. This special occasions will be loaded with possibilities for laughter, learning, healing and international goodwill. The tour will offer four kinds of events in each community:

1. Laughter Days: Red clown noses are being sold by local Laughter Liasions during the months preceding our appearance. It is announced on the press, radio and TV that everyone will wear their red noses on that particular day, in support of world peace.

2. Laughter Demonstrations: We will stage public demonstrations of Laughter Club exercises under the guidance of experts. This could be at public parks, school gymnasiums, health clubs, or community centers.

3. We will present public lectures on Healing Power of Humour and Laughter. We can also present workshops for health care professionals, educators, and business people. We can present professional, continuing education workshops for health professionals, as well as humour and productivity seminars for business and industry.

HOW TO BECOME A LAUGHTER LIASION?

Laughter Liaisons are people who volunteer their time and energy to bring the WLT to their communities. These laughter lovers help the WLT find hosts in business, healthcare, education and elsewhere. Offers of assistance have already started pouring in from the United States, England, Canada, Australia, Germany, Singapore, Dubai, and Japan. They are asking us, "How can I start a Laughter Club (like the ones that are doing so much good in India) in my city?" and, "Will the World Laughter Tour be coming to my city this year?" We are delighted that so many wonderful people - whom we have nicknamed "Laughter Lovers", or LL's would like to help make this laughter movement a success. Now, our challenge is to organise and coordinate the efforts of Laughter Lovers around the world so that the message of laughter and importance of humour travels to every continent. To accomplish this historic mission we need LLs around the world to help us identify organisations that would want to host the WLT. These organisations will pay the travel, lodging and lecture fees to bring the WLT to their area.

BENEFITS TO THE ORGANISATIONS

Benefits include the publicity, the education and the opportunity to raise funds for their worthy causes. The funds can be raised by charging admission to lectures, selling clown noses, books, tapes and t-shirts and charging entry fees to special events like All Fools Day, Laughter Contest, Gibberish Contest, Smile Contests and selling advertising space in programme booklets.

WHO ARE THE SPONSORS?

Among the likely sponsoring organisations might be corporations, hospitals, universities, civic groups, or professional associations. The host most likely already believes in the importance of laughter and humour and shares the vision of World Laughter. Or, the host has an interest in understanding and learning more about 'Yogic Laughter Therapy', or wants to foster Laughter Clubs such as those are prevalent throughout India.

Host organisations stand to raise significant funds and they will attract enormous positive attention through local, national and worldwide publicity. Organisations might act individually to become hosts or two or more organisations might partner to host a WLT event.

If you have already understood the remarkable power of laughter and humour, you already qualify as a 'Laughter Lover'. You can help us support the WLT and bring it to your area by identifying potential hosts and either contacting them for us, or sending us their names and contact information and we will get in touch with them.

WE WILL SEND INFORMATION

To help you get started, you will receive a Press Kit containing an overvied of the WLT. The credentials of the expert team of Kataria, Buxman and Wilson. Newspaper articles about the World Laughter Movement articles about Laughter Clubs and news releases for your local media will be included along with 10-minute video showing ABC-TV's report on Laughter Clubs of India as well as people using laughter as medicine in U.S.A.. Tell us more about yourself and your interest in laughter. We want ideas about possible host organisations in your area. And, as we become aware of them, we will also network you with other Laughter Lovers in your area.For more details contact:

World Laughter Tour
P.O. Box: 30426
Gahanna Oh 43230 U.S.A.
Email: Info@worldlaughtertour.com
Laugh@vsnl.com.
Website: www.worldlaughtertour. com.